t3

J

A Certain Slant of Light

Advance Copy

A Certain Slant of Light

Duncan White

www.hhousebooks.com

Paperback ISBN: 978-1-910688-97-7

Cover design by Ken Dawson Creative Covers
Typeset by Polgarus Studio

Published in the UK

Holland House Books
Holland House
47 Greenham Road
Newbury, Berkshire RG14 7HY
United Kingdom

www.hhousebooks.com

for Matilda
and for Alex

Contents

There's a certain Slant of light,
Winter Afternoons –
That oppresses, like the Heft
Of Cathedral Tunes –

Heavenly Hurt, it gives us –
We can find no scar,
But internal difference,
Where the Meanings, are –

None may teach it – Any –
'Tis the Seal Despair –
An imperial affliction
Sent us of the Air –

When it comes, the Landscape listens –
Shadows – hold their breath –
When it goes, 'tis like the Distance
On the look of Death –

Emily Dickinson

One

After the Crash

Happy those drivers who, seeing a steep descent before them are not inspired with a diabolical impulse to take off all brakes and dash to destruction.

Isadora Duncan

Reality: what we run up against in our journey towards death; hence, what we are interested in.

Vilem Flusser

Some time before sleep became impossible, I dreamt I was walking on the Promenade des Anglais. A warm breeze stirred the branches of the king palms high above my head while in the Bay of Angels a cruise ship lay like an iceberg. Out to sea, black clouds banked against the horizon but for now those around me – joggers, men and women with dogs, children running into the waves – moved in an atmosphere of peace and calm. It struck me then that I was no longer in a dream but a photograph, one I had cut from a magazine many years before; or perhaps I had clipped the picture that morning after I had woken and written down my dream, something I did more and more in the wake of our child's death.

Yet such scenes might just as likely have been triggered by my one and only journey to Nice when, on exiting the gloomy interiors of the train station, I was blinded by the sunlight that seemed to penetrate my body so that I might, in that instant, dissolve as I made my way beyond the pickpockets and the down-and-outs toward the sea. I now realise that the desire to disappear, to fall away into the same light, would plague me during those days and months and even now as something both longed for and feared. But as I passed through the narrow streets I thought only of the painters lured to the Riviera where one's gaze is free to travel far further than usual, making it possible to pick out the looming form of Alpine peaks hundreds of miles in the distance which would remain quite invisible were it not for the sensation of cobalt blues and pinks rising out of the only reality we can truly understand: that of our imaginations. But it may be my dream had its origins in a film or a book, maybe I had not made the journey at all one summer in my youth, for, as with that strange condition of all dreams and dreamers, or of those who have suffered loss and can no longer connect who they are with who they had been, I wasn't clear in my own mind whether I was taking part in events or merely observing them from an unknown vantage; yet it appeared perfectly natural to be taking the air not far from where Isadora Duncan, who had already lost two children in a car accident, was killed by an automobile.

~

By 1906, the same year that the house in which she was born was lost to the earthquake that destroyed San Francisco, Duncan's dance was celebrated and revered in all of the great cities of the world from Los Angeles to New York, Berlin to St Petersburg, from Paris to London to Budapest, where she was pursued feverishly by wild-eyed fans and paparazzi alike. Rodin, Picabia, Cocteau and Gertrude Stein were among her greatest admirers. When she was near you, or when she danced, Duncan was like a wave of life that passed over, Hart Crane wrote when he saw her on a Cleveland stage.

Given the fervour inspired by Duncan's dance, it is perhaps unfortunate for those of us looking back with aching hearts hoping to catch a glimpse of what we have missed that Isadora Duncan refused all her life to be filmed. In the many books about Duncan, including her own, there are the details of her life, stacked in order like a vast lumber-room of incidents and trivia, and yet Duncan's dance remains forever distant as if it can be made out only in the quickening of shadows or in a draft passing silently through a room left empty, here and there inspiring eddies of dust. Even as her

4

greatest friends and her greatest rivals embraced the new technology of ghosts and shadows, Duncan feared her dance would be ripped away from her, that it would be copied and trivialised, rendered the property of those she could not see or show directly how to construct shape and form out of the interconnection of movement and theme.

On September 14th 1927, after Ivan Nikolenko had taken her to dinner and won her trust and who insisted on making the first ever film of her dance the following day, Isadora Duncan climbed into the Amilcar Grand Sport of Benoit Falchetto, threw her shawl once more around her throat and cried, *Adieu, mes amis, je vais a la glorie!* The long fringe of her crimson scarf fell over the side of the car and caught in the spokes of the left rear wheel. As soon as Falchetto roared away her neck was broken and she was dead.

Looking back into the strange absence left by the car accident (one of the many car accidents that would, like the invention of film, mark out the modern world from the one that came before) I find it hard to believe Isadora Duncan had chosen death over film. And yet there was the darkness, the doubts, the regrets; the hallucinations of black cats in her rooms, birds about her head and coffins in the snow. In April 1913, her children were drowned in the Seine after the new Ford they were in misfired and ran away from its stranded driver, gloved and suited, crank in hand, who could only watch in astonishment as the black machine shot forward as if under the power of some diabolical force, like a moving camera swallowing everything in its path, across Boulevard Bourdon, jumped the pavement opposite and careened down the grassy

embankment into the river. According to those who saw their bodies recovered from the dark waters, the two children died clinging to the neck of their drowned nurse their faces stricken with indescribable terror; Duncan was thrown, once and for all, into the haunted world of mothers and fathers who have to bury their young. Fourteen years later, on the day Isadora Duncan's own coffin travelled by train from Nice to Paris, a storm blew in from the Balearic Sea and the rain poured down. On the coffin's arrival at the crematorium at Père Lechaise, where a crowd estimated by those who were there to be made up of 10,000 souls had gathered, this picture of Isadora Duncan and her children, Deidre and Patrick, stood on a table near the body between burning tapers.

~

In my dream, as in life, there is nothing that marks the place where Isadora Duncan was killed along the Promenade des Anglais: only the pale smoothing over of anything and everything that has come before and gone. As I woke from the view of that glittering sea, both a picture of emptiness and an empty picture, I wasn't sure why Isadora Duncan had come into my dreams at all. But then I saw the footprint I now see every morning hanging on black thread next to a window. The little print, darkest where the soles and toes had been pushed against the paper and lightest where the white river-like lines tracing the unique pathways of the tiny foot had not taken the ink, had been made on the morning my second child was born dead. On her grave in a cemetery on the very outskirts of north London where she is buried in a box just larger than a violin case, it reads: Born Asleep.

But this isn't right. A dead baby is nothing like a baby that is sleeping and, lying somewhere between wakefulness and dream, it always seemed strange to me that anyone confronted with a human body that is no longer breathing, whose heart no longer pushes blood through its veins, where there is no longer life in every breath, every hair and every invisible cell, that anyone could connect sleeping with death. Perhaps that was why sleep would later become so difficult for me.

On that morning in the early dawn light which always caught me by surprise the shape of the footprint seemed to float in front of me as if it had been left in the sand and would soon wash away; or as if it had been laid in the early spring frost and would very soon be melted by the sun, passing away from me as completely as the person who left it there. Waking from that dream I wasn't clear if the footprint was connected somehow with the dance of Isadora Duncan, unseen except in the fragments of evidence that had been left behind. What is clear is that the print floating in the light like dream material and which I now think of (to the extent that I can think of anything) as a form of travel writing, marked the first step on a journey along pathways that would never connect, that would lead to dead ends and empty rooms, but which I had to follow and set down somehow in these notes.

Isadora Duncan's dance, I now realise, did not exist in the past or in the present but in some place in between, perhaps the same place my daughter had taken her first steps without me. Before events at the hospital, Anne and I passed a happy hour together – perhaps our last – cutting the shapes of birds out of yellow paper to hang above the new baby's bed. When we returned later to the room we stood for a long time staring at the yellow birds hanging in the empty air. The place we once knew had been taken over by a silence that would give way to screaming and rotten, rotting words that would eventually push us apart. Over the following months as I became more and more exercised by what wasn't there so the life that *was* there and which had up until that point been vividly present, began to recede. In many ways, my notes on fearful events – car accidents, bodies falling through the air, and the rest – stand in for something which even today I cannot bring myself to admit. And while it's true Duncan might have come into my dreams as a part of this feverish note-taking, it could also be because those of us who have been left stranded by the randomness of a child's death inevitably begin to seek out patterns long before we realise we are doing it.

Yet it is just as likely to be because the dreaded red batik shawl Isadora Duncan brought with her from New York City and insisted on wearing that night in September 1927 made of heavy crepe two yards long and five feet wide with fringes at either end of eighteen inches in length was adorned with a vast yellow bird. I have never seen that bird, but I'm sure it would have looked like the birds we hung over an empty bed. I wondered if certain animals, certain winged creatures, have the power to escape our dreams and the destructive world out of which they are born only to be pursued in vain by those they leave behind. Sometime later, it would occur to me that I had without realising it become a collector of such lost events; a hoarder of pictures that no longer connected with a past but which had come, instead, to stand in place of an absent heart.

1

In the winter of 1970 John Latham was seriously injured in a head-on car collision on an icy road between Cambridge and London. It took over an hour to cut Latham from the wreckage. The police telephoned his wife, Barbara Steveni, telling her it was touch and go. Latham's chest had been crushed with the impact of the crash. No one thought I would survive, Latham later recalled, my lungs were lacerated, and nine of my ribs were broken.

The following winter, what was left of Latham's car, as well as documents relating to the crash and his stay in Clare Hall Hospital, were included in the exhibition, Art and Economics, at the Hayward Gallery on London's Southbank. By all accounts, the exhibition – which to this day remains the

gallery's least attended – looked more like an office of records than an art exhibition. Latham's contribution, a work he entitled simply, *Hospital*, and only part of which continues to exist, was made up of a series of X-Rays of his chest, hospital notes, the remains of the car and photographs of care-staff going about their duties. Visitors could survey the evidence of what had happened that night and in the weeks that followed but there was no work as such, nothing made by the artist in order to express what, if anything, his near-death experience might have meant. For the disoriented visitor a computer terminal had been set up *to answer questions.*

I soon discovered that there was something self-defeating about the research I was involved in and my notes – pages and pages of notes – seemed to be tracing out holes in the air. As with *Hospital*, so many of the artworks from that time no longer exist, either because they never existed in the first place or because they only existed for a time or because the works themselves were obliterated, smashed to pieces in the very process of being made. All that was left was fragments, like the burnt cover page of a portfolio issue of The Metropolitan Seminars in Art dedicated to the artist as visionary found among the ashes of art history textbooks and encyclopaedias set fire to by Latham in 1966. For hours on end, I would look at the images and feel suddenly as if I were losing my balance. Who were those people (I have since discovered that the tall man wearing sunglasses is Barry Flanagan) watching the fires go up? What is that time from which everything is gone, the place, the works – and soon, all those who were there? Toiling over such an unreliable catalogue of unverifiable works, I became increasingly disoriented and found myself wondering if Latham had any memory of that night in December 1970 on the outskirts of north London, or was it the case that he could only gaze like the rest of us at the photographs taken from the time and wonder who that person must have been that had come so close to death. In one of the pictures taken in the hospital, Latham appears to be unconscious as the nurses go about their duties, and I can't help but think of Rembrandt's *The Anatomy Lesson*, and of Eliot's patient etherised upon a table, caught between one world and the next.

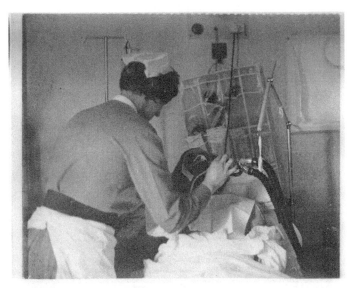

There is something disconcerting about a person photographed with their eyes closed. On the one hand, it reveals a terrible vulnerability as we are permitted suddenly to see them in a way that they will never see themselves; on the other, they appear to have slipped our attentions completely. More like a mask made before burial, the photograph, in its stillness, is closer to death than any sleeping body. Latham's hospital pictures remind me of Édouard Vuillard's self-portrait with eyes closed. How did Vuillard paint this picture I often ask myself? It couldn't have been done using a mirror. I can only assume that the painter worked from a photograph, for how else could he see his face without his own eyes or, as it were, from within his own mind. Perhaps to be inside ourselves is to see what the camera sees; to be an outsider along with everybody else. The same is true of this picture of André Breton. He is there.

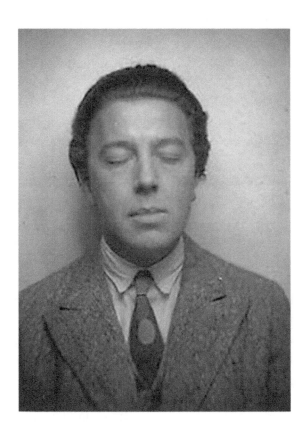

But that can only mean he is *not* there. Disappearing in this way in front of his likeness amounts, in the end, to an image of abandonment or on-going escape, but from what and to where nobody can know. Perhaps every car accident, whether it's that of Jayne Mansfield or of Albert Camus, produces an image we already have in our minds like preparing a room for someone who we know is about to arrive but never does except as something gone. An event that exists in a place between one time and another, in the places we travel to when we close our eyes. Latham's nearness (to death and to me), however improbable, was important then. But it masked a greater distance that I was only beginning to understand and which seemed to exist in all of the pictures. In the time since Anne and I returned from that other hospital – not the one in Potters Bar where Latham was treated and which no longer exists but a hospital not far from there which has now also gone – I promised to remember (to whom exactly I'm not sure) three details from that 24 hours of hospitalisation which, no matter what else would fade or become blanked out and lost to the confusion of the coming months and years, would remain within reach somehow: like a piece of what was missing, something tangible that I could carry with me.

The first of these memories was the black spot on the ultrasound that a doctor pointed to — *that should be moving*, she said. The heart., you can clearly see there is no heartbeat. But what I was seeing was only an echo, like the sonar images fisherman use to scout the dark waters beneath their boats. We see the picture because sound comes back, I remember thinking much later. Since then it has become all but impossible to look at any black and white image without seeing this shadow. This is especially true of pictures intended to evidence some form of accident; a moment when all control was lost. Instead of machine-made images linked without question to the things they portrayed, I was confronted with false outlines, a place made up of shapes abstracted from an invisible world no longer available to those who had survived, where all that remains for us is to report on its destruction.

2

In the autumn of that year, finding myself quite unable to work, I travelled to Paris; in the first of many wrong connections, under the illusion that John Latham had once known the Romanian immigrant artist, Isadore Isou, who fled to France at the end of the Second World War, and had recently died. To make things worse, there was no chance of seeing any works by Isidore Isou. After 1968 the painter, poet and self-proclaimed cinema-maker destroyed every painting, sculpture, poem or film he made, and from then specialised in works that could not exist except as objects that for whatever reason, had been wiped out. But I had learned of a ledger in which Isou kept detailed notes of every one of his works created before being burned, crushed, thrown into the Seine or dissolved in acid. In the weeks before I left for Paris, the existence of this ledger took on an almost magical presence in my mind. If this hidden record of what was lost could be found then there may be others –so I told myself – that I could also find. The ledger had been left with Michael D., an impoverished Englishman who had, in his words, *run away from that illogical isle* sometime in the 1970s *when everything was closing down.* Quite by chance, he found himself living illegally in the apartment below Isou.

Having left in something of a hurry, I was badly prepared

for the trip. It took me half of the week or so I had there to track Michael down to a tiny flat in the Fifteenth Arrondisssement where he lived alone. The concierge, who seemed most amused by my enquiries, pointed me toward a set of dilapidated stairs. You have come, as they say in England, to see a man about a dog? Michael D.'s one room apartment was on the top floor and his door was unlocked as he had told me it would be on the telephone the day before. I found him in front of the sink, dressed all in white and ghostly thin. I was astonished to discover that Michael, who had lived (or survived) in Paris for three decades on the barest of means, spoke all but a few words of French. *Knowing one language is bad enough,* he told me, I *came here to be free of all that. I hardly ever hear English and that's fine with me.* He was so thin he seemed to hang in space; when he moved I worried he might disappear completely or crumble into dust. He had lived beneath Isou for less than a year before moving on and it wasn't clear how he had come into possession of the ledger. *So you have come to see the book*, he said and he bent down, quite easily despite his age and decrepit appearance, to reach for a box beneath his bed, that seemed to be held in the air by a pile of shoes each one as worn through as the next . *I didn't much like Isou*, Michael said. *He was terribly rude about women. I suppose he had some interesting friends. And, as you know, I never lock my door...*

The ledger listed hundreds of works that had been made and then destroyed by Isou over a number of years. Each handwritten entry recorded a title and the materials used. It also noted how each object had been destroyed – most seem to have been burned. None of the entries were dated but referred instead to a day of the week or a time of day. Where appropriate, dimensions were marked, and some of the works were of a significant size. One painting titled Red was eight feet square. The description reads: acrylic on canvas. Colour bands. Mainly blue. Burned. There was a series of sculptures made of lead. Each was marked as melted, and I realised they had been made from the same piece of lead until Isou moulded the final figure in the sequence, recording it: melted, thrown away. Seeing that each lead-work in the series carried for its title a different personal pronoun – Vladimir, Constantin, Francois etc – I wondered if the set was based on people he knew. *Not exactly,* Michael said. *They were the names of his forefathers. I don't know if he was doing away with them once and for all or if he meant instead to give them eternal life,* Michael observed.

One piece, entitled Things He Had to Say About the Rain, referred to nothing but one hundred and eleven birds, pigeons, sparrows, starlings. There was no note as to how they were destroyed and I must have looked at Michael with some alarm. Michael laughed and told me not to worry. *He didn't kill any birds. He let them go. For him, there was no difference.*

Later that day, as he poured us the tea he had made in a bright red jug, Michael, in tones I was becoming used to, pointed out that Isou could have made it all up. That these entries could be nothing but the fancies of a madman. The thought must have crossed my mind but I wanted to believe in what I was reading; I wanted the entries to refer to something even if what they referred to was gone.

As we went through the ledger, I noticed that there were

names beside a number of the works. One painting, called Little Death, which jumped out at me then and had been made, according to the ledger, from cotton wool mixed with motor oil, was inscribed with the name Maurice. Another, made from paper and spit, with the name Tristan. It turned out that these were the names of those Isou had nominated to destroy particular works. *Well,* Michael seemed to admit, *he didn't want to do it all himself. I don't know why.* Towards the end of the ledger, and much to my relief, I found Michael's name beside a work called, Missing Lines. Michael shrugged. *He must have asked me because I was his neighbour and it was convenient. Isou was always running about.* So he wasn't making it up? I said. Michael smiled. *If that's what the ledger says. The truth is, I don't remember. — I do remember one of his films,* Michael later said. *You haven't asked me about his films.*

One night, Isou all but fell through the door carrying a heavy Russian-made projector and pushed everything aside with his foot so that he could set it down here, Michael said, waving at the air in front of me, *and point it at the wall. I couldn't understand the film at all,* Michael told me. *It seemed to be all jumbled up. Nothing was in order. One thing kept crashing into the next and it jumped around so much it made me dizzy. But I remember one particularly grainy section of a naked toddler walking along an empty beach. That's me! Isou screamed when the boy appeared. It's me! He kept saying. Look at his nose! And he had tears in his eyes,* Michael recalled. *I think Isou liked to see himself before he could speak, or read, or remember. Maybe that's why none of his films made sense. Or why he couldn't put his stories in*

21

a straight line. But he was quite mad by then, Michael said. *And I'm still not sure if that tiny boy could have been Idsidore Isou.*

Many of the details of that trip have been lost to my memory. Overall, it was a failure. I had hoped to verify that the ledger was genuine but despite my best efforts I came away with the distinct impression that the opposite must be the case and was left with the sense I had wasted time and money, both of which were short back then. I must have been feeling this way while waiting for a break in the traffic on Rue Saint Jacques, not far from the fountains of the Jardin de Luxembourg, where cars and motorbikes come quickly round a bend, when Michael leaned into me and said, *you know this is where Roland Barthes was killed crossing the road?* I had no idea what to do with this information.

We stood in silence and watched the cars and motorcycles go by before I realised Michael had drifted away from me and

I was alone. I was getting used to these disappearances, often quite sudden, of people coming and going as if they were moving in and out of focus, put into the scene by an unseen camera-cut only to be taken away again, at the mercy of the same mechanical technique which had, as it were, brought them into the world. At one point during our conversation that afternoon, Michael had lent back in his chair and closed his eyes as if it was suddenly all too much. I thought this was a strange thing to do in the company of someone he had just met and it struck me that he was acting as if I wasn't there. When he opened his eyes, I asked Michael if I could take his photograph but he seemed so confused by my request that my embarrassment made me put the camera away. I regret that now.

I never saw Michael again and sometimes I wonder if I had met a ghost. The only verification for what I remember happening during those days in Paris is the portrait photo I had made in a photo-booth stationed behind an escalator that led down to the metro at Gare du  Nord in order to access the national library. I must not have returned to the library with the necessary paperwork as I recently found the picture tucked into a copy of Huizinga's *Erasmus of Rotterdam*. At first I didn't recognise myself and this created a terrible nervousness when I realised I was basing what I knew of that time on the work of someone else, someone I had once been but no longer knew. How could I trust even what was written there in my own hand? And yet, what else could I do? I had read stories of ex-soldiers who on returning to civilian life held onto photographs taken of them while in active service as among their most treasured possessions. The picture provided their only access to a time when they had to become another person, a killing machine capable of terrible things. And I realised I had done the opposite – perhaps out of guilt, I had banished all images of myself from my home – covered them over as if I was in the process always of passing from this world into the next. Seeing the small square picture triggered the recollection of a pigeon turned black with dirt making its idle way along a metro platform despite the fact that we were hundreds of feet below ground and without any obvious route to the sky. Eventually, I decided to find another place to cross Rue Saint Jacques.

Looking over my notes, which were strangely scientific then compared to my usually haphazard style, I seem to have taken a particular interest in a passage in the writings of Roland Barthes where he describes himself posing to have his photograph taken. One day, he writes, an excellent photographer took my picture. Ordinarily, he could not stand to have his photograph taken, although he did on many occasions do just that. Whenever he posed for the camera, setting his body and his facial features into a position that looked, so to speak, like Roland Barthes, he felt as if he were turning himself into a picture even before the camera captured his likeness on the film. He watched himself as if he had become his own spectator, imitating not so much himself as the appearance of himself. This caused a painful sense of falsehood: a sense that he existed suddenly in imitation, but of who or what he did not know: as if he were playing a part in some unspoken fabrication. But, on that day, the photographer seemed to have captured something else. *I believed I could read in his image the distress of a recent bereavement,* Barthes writes. *For once photography had delivered me to myself.* Indeed, the photograph seemed to reveal something that would have remained invisible, even non-existent, if it had not been taken.

But when he discovered this same portrait published on

the cover of his book something had changed. Barthes was horrified. Instead of an appearance he was faced with how much had already disappeared. It was as if, he writes, I saw myself after I was dead.

Looking back, *Camera Lucida* seems like a strange choice of guidebook given the condition I was in but Barthes' writing, which I had returned to purely by accident (in the same way that he had, as it were, come to his own end), seemed less to me then a book about photography so much as a mourning diary written a year after his mother passed away and whose photograph taken when she was a young woman before her son was born caused him a particular form of torment.

One other guidebook from that time, later leading me on another of my incoherent journeyings, was Winfried Georg Sebald's interminable ramble through East Anglia. *What is this*, Anne said to me once, holding the dog-eared copy of *Rings of Saturn* out in front of her, turning it around in her hands like it was an object from outer space. *It's completely random*, she complained. *What is he doing? Why is he doing it?* But the same thoughts had never troubled me. Instead, the pathways of words and sentences traced out ahead and spiralling back on themselves, appeared clear in some way and I followed them mindlessly, I now know, in the hope that they might lead me to what I would never find.

Nor had I taken any particular interest in the so-called biographies of these writers, in the nefarious fictions of other people's lives, until I discovered that both Roland Barthes and W.G. Sebald died in car accidents far apart from one another in events that were otherwise unconnected, cut off as it were, mid-sentence. Perhaps, in keeping these notes, I was not acting entirely under my own will, it occurred to me then, but had been set to a task of someone else's choosing, taking up where they had left off. Either way, I could not know for sure. It turned out, of course, that Roland Barthes died a month after the road accident from injuries he had sustained to his chest.

In the years since, my memories of that street corner in Paris have become confused in my mind with the X-Rays of John Latham's lungs made after his crash in 1971 at the hospital in Potter's Bar. When I first saw these X-Rays, revealing, as it were, the internal life of the artist, I peered for a long time at the blotches of black suspended within the grey and white clouds of the exposure, as if I were looking into an empty room. I think it was then that I appreciated just what Barthes was describing when he rediscovered that portrait of himself. While in Paris or during the time since, I failed to find any images relating to the death of Roland Barthes in the early spring of 1982, and it could be the case that Latham's chest X-Rays have come to stand in for this gap in memory. Having said that, the confusion could just as well be because I have kept copies of drawings made by Barthes that only came to light in the wake of the writer's death. Whenever I look at these drawings I am reminded on the one hand of the bronchial fibres that make up human lungs and on the other, they appear to me to be maps showing the chaotic web of streets and alleyways of some fantastical city, one that can only be accessed, perhaps, by the victims of road accidents.

3

On my way back from Paris, the train pulled into St Pancras so slowly that I began to wonder if it was as reluctant as I was to leave the unreality of moving landscapes and return finally to the too-real world of fixed destinations. I picked up a newspaper and made my way through the crowd to the underground only to read, as I drifted downwards beneath the earth via the metallic medium of the Kings Cross escalators, that the most expensive work of art ever to be sold had just been auctioned at Sotheby's. This fact alone would have held little interest if it were not the case that the subject of the painting, as the newspaper described it, had an immediate bearing on my state of mind.

Taking my seat on a train while paying little attention to where I was heading or to what purpose, I could not take my eyes off the reproduction of the large silkscreen print known *as Double Disaster*, which Andy Warhol had once made with the help of his friends from two equally sized canvases in 1963. The left-hand panel shows again and again an image, probably cut from another newspaper, of a car collided with a tree. You can make out the shape of a body strewn through the car's interior repeated, as it were, eternally. My attention, however, was drawn to the second panel, an empty silvery façade that seems to shimmer in a ghostly reflection of what has just taken place or of what is yet to happen, as if waiting its turn in the queue. What struck me about the article was that the editors at the newspaper, preoccupied by the apparent irony of the content considering its new price-tag, had chosen only to reproduce the panel showing the car accident, deciding, I assume, that they couldn't dedicate any more of their evening edition to a blank space. While comparatively insignificant, given everything that was happening at the time, the omission troubled me immensely. So much was already gone, I remember thinking. And now this.

During that winter in 2013 I could not get the missing panel, which despite its size goes largely unnoticed even in the literature, out of my mind. Of course the panel was anything but empty or blank and this missing half put me in mind of a letter written to me by Anne some weeks after we had decided to be apart. A friend, who thought I should read it, passed the letter on, but the matters it contained were all the more striking for what they did not say. Anne had been struggling to find time to work on her book. She mentioned a broken door-handle. That the early frosts had killed the autumn bulbs. Oddly – although I'm not sure I thought it odd at the time – she had left a sheet blank. On the following page she mentions that she had woken that morning to discover the 30-foot yew at the back of what had been our home had blown down in the night. *Look how far you can see*, the same friend who delivered the letter said to her that morning. But as she writes, *I'm not sure my view is much improved.*

I traced my finger along the final words before folding the letter away and locking it in a drawer. Ever since that time, the letter and the missing half of the picture in the newspaper have come to overlap in my mind as if the two things were intimately related even if I could find nothing that might connect one with the other in any way.

For the remaining weeks of that year I could not bring myself to reply to the letter. It was not until I travelled, on another of my uncertain errands, to the reading rooms of the Victoria and Albert Museum that I was able to put pen to paper again. I remember probing through the eccentric pile of books, journals and magazines ordered up from the repositories I assumed were in basements beneath my feet in the manner of someone who knows their search is hopeless but who goes on regardless as if the distraction of looking will save them from something far worse.

I was there in order to look through the record of yet another road accident. In this version of what seemed to me to be an endlessly recurring event, the writer and two of his friends drove into the barren lands east of Los Angeles and threw a new Royal Model X Typewriter from the window of their Buick. Each page records another lost fragment of the

wreckage strewn along the side of the road for some two hundred feet. Various machine-parts – the carriage assembly, feed roller, ribbon spool, tab bar – had travelled some way into the desert. Others were found wedged into the dirt like weeds springing from cracks in the ground. For some time I gazed at the faces of these young men, who in turn were gazing at what they had done, and I wondered what it was they were attempting to write by disintegrating so completely the mechanisation of written words. But I could read no trace of emotion in their features; there was no sense of remorse for what had happened, or excitement at the results. Instead they held up the evidence, as if that was all they could do, offering themselves as a point of reference or to give the pictures scale, and I realised that they were no closer to what had taken place in the desert than I was in that London museum.

I was overcome then by a feeling of dizziness as if I were no longer in that old library but instead looking down from a great height on so many lost things. Vertigo was becoming familiar to me. I would later come upon a photograph of Barry Flannagan, John Latham's student and friend, making his film, *Hole in the Sea*. The photograph shows Gerry Schum at the extreme limit of a fire engine's ladder extended horizontally over the freezing waters of the North Sea. Schum must be suspended at least thirty feet in the air in order to achieve the correct perspective. Observing this figure, lying prostrate over the incoming tide, a picture that had come out of a past more real to me then than my own story, I found myself convinced suddenly that I must have taken this photograph: even though I know it was made by Ursula Wevers almost a decade before I was born. And I began to wonder if the problem, as with all forms of so-called evidence, was not so much what had disappeared but what form the disappearance was beginning to take among the things it had replaced.

On leaving the library and making my way along Exhibition Road towards Kensington Gardens, I thought again of the newspaper copy of those doubled disasters, and I felt a sudden panic to get back and read Anne's letter once more. But when I unlocked the drawer and unfolded the pages nothing had changed. Only the blank page seemed to be saying anything. I looked around. Each of the many printed words, like the pictures I had collected showing so much of what was smashed, seemed to me like a room that no longer exists, yet, there it was waiting for me to pick up where I left off or to finish what I can never get done. These were places I had been visiting, as it were, on and off for many years. But what had once felt like a form of affinity – of continuity – now came back to me as a series of shocks, like the car crash copied in silver and black repeated over and over again, leading always back to its disastrous end which may also be a beginning for those with emptied hearts.

The artist's studio, 2215 Echo Park Avenue, Los Angeles, 1963. On wall, *Smash* (1963. Oil on canvas, 72 × 67″).

Later that night, unable to sleep, it was with some surprise that I read in one of Robert Walser's travel stories of the lost, so gay and light they hardly seem weighted down by the paper they are printed on or the ink that holds each word in place, of how, one day, he went for a walk and realised that our longing for happiness seems far more beautiful, always far more sensitive, more significant and all in all probably far more desirable than happiness itself, which perhaps need not even exist. Perhaps, in the same way, I was embarking on a new version of the newspaper's car crash picture, repeating the gruesome image so that it lost its effect. I could not know for sure. All I could do, I now thought, was to continue bound as I was to these cyphers, giving names to a reality I could possess only by rendering it unreal.

4

In a way, Jackson Pollock had to die the way he did,
crashing his car up.

Andy Warhol

On Saturday October 13th, 1990, Hans Namuth was killed in
a car accident. His vehicle collided with another car at the
intersection of Long Lane and Stephen Hands path in East
Hampton, New York. Namuth was on his way home having
attended a screening of his new film about his friend Jasper
Johns. He had been making photographic portraits of
painters and sculptors for forty years, and his photographs of
Jackson Pollock, catching him, brushless, in the act of pouring
and dripping and throwing paint, would make Pollock a
household name. Yet, in an interview ten years earlier in the
spring of 1980, Namuth, who rarely spoke about his work or
appeared in public, told a journalist that he did not know
what made him want to take photographs of artists. The
journalist had been attempting to interview Namuth for
several months and was convinced the German émigré would
not appear when, as promised at precisely midday, the door
to Namuth's modest studio – into which the journalist had
been ushered only moments before – swung open. *We shook
hands and before either of us spoke he did something I will*

never forget, the journalist recalls. He reached across the table and closed my notebook. Then he smiled. *Let me tell you everything*, Hans Namuth said.

When he spoke, the journalist writes, Namuth's warm accented English seemed to spread slowly about the room like a lighted candle picking out details – a yellow chair, a stack of fashion magazines, a bright red Italian coffee pot – bringing brief animation to objects that would otherwise be lost to the gloom. The journalist could not take his eyes off Namuth and throughout their conversation he found himself wondering if the man in front of him was real. He certainly wore the world-weary look of those who travelled relentlessly and it was all he could do, the journalist recalls, not to check if the dirt still clung to Namuth's boots. He had returned from Central America, revisiting a village high in the hills of Guatemala, a village known as *Todos Santos*, *All Saints* or the *Place of Two Crosses*, which Namuth had first photographed in 1946. *Nothing had changed*, he told the journalist looking around the room so that the reporter had to wonder if the photographer was referring to the box-like studio rather than the place in his memory. *Yet everything was different*, he sighed. *But forgive me*, he said. *That is not the place to begin.* And he seemed eager to go back as far as he could, to retrace the order of events that had brought him to where they were now.

Namuth first left Germany in 1933 after being detained by the Gestapo for distributing leaflets denouncing Adolf Hitler. *I can still feel their hands on me*, he told the journalist. Hans F. Namuth, who had recently joined the Nazi Party, agreed a release and sent his son to France that September with a fourteen-day exit visa. With the same resourcefulness that would see him through his life, the teenage Hans travelled from Paris to the Pyrenees where he spent a summer on a farm among Quakers. There he felt a nearness to being happy that seemed to push happiness away. He longed to see Marianne Stark with whom he had had an intense four-month love affair in Paris before she moved to Tel Aviv. That August he resolved, as he put it, to cease living in his head, and spent the following year in pursuit of Marianne. He travelled through much of the Middle East and the Mediterranean before he tracked her down to Athens, where, he was horrified to discover, she had been married the previous spring.

Exhausted, alone, and beset by a sense of emptiness, Namuth, for want of anything else to do, joined his school-friend the photographer Georg Reisner, a fellow German, specialising in portraits of wealthy islanders in Puerto de Pollensa. Tall, blue-eyed, with dark black hair, Reisner was electric: *like a light in the dark*, Namuth said. *I remember the light, and the way men and women walked around in the sun as if nothing had happened or as if nothing ever would.* Namuth quickly learned how to take photographs and at the end of the season in Majorca he and Georg returned to Paris where they began a career taking snapshots for the city's numerous picture magazines and newspapers clambering for images of a fast-changing world. They worked tirelessly and as the winter passed in the city, the two men longed once more for the warmth and freedom of the islands. *It would be our final sojourn*, Namuth remembered looking around the studio for something that might compare with the brevity of human peace. In the summer of 1936 the pair returned to Majorca where they received an assignment, almost immediately upon arrival, from *Vu* magazine in France to photograph the Worker's Olympiad in Barcelona.

The day after they arrived in the Catalan city on 18th July 1936 the Spanish Civil War erupted. *I remember*, Namuth told the journalist, *I woke up in the pension where we were staying to sounds of what I thought were fireworks. I thought the festive event had started.* It turned out the sound he had heard was machine gun fire. The pair covered different districts, rushing to beat the reports, selling what they saw first to *Vu* and then to newspapers and supplements, to *Berliner Illustrirte Zeitung* and *Münchner Illustrierte Presse*.

On August 19, 1936, the first issue of *Die Volks-Illustrierte* printed a collage by John Heartfield in support of the popular front. The image, incorporating *Liberty Leading the People* by Eugene Delacroix, painted a century before, combined with a photograph taken by Namuth and Reisner in the street, was printed alongside the interview in 1980 and it seemed to describe the fabrication – for good or ill – inherent in any retelling of events. Despite the clarity of detail or the clinically disinterested style of the journalist's interview with Namuth, it seemed less and less clear to me who was telling Namuth's story, as though something was happening in several places at once, so that the actual location of events would remain uncertain like those figures in the street.

Reisner and I, Namuth's story goes on, shared a Rolleiflex and a Leica – lightweight, portable and fast – frequently swapping cameras so that it became impossible to tell who took which image. Most were sold under the signature

Namuth/Reisner as if the two men had merged. As the bloody conflict intensified it became increasingly clear that they could no longer remain and at the end of 1936 Namuth and Reisner returned to Paris.

For the next few years, the two men were separated and Namuth was alone. *I slowed down, and like everybody else I was afraid*, Namuth said. When war was declared on his homeland, life in France was thrown into turmoil once more. Under orders of the French government, he and other German nationals were interned first at the Colombe sports stadium, in Paris and then at the Camps des Etrangers, in the Loirre where in the absence of drafted locals he helped bring in the harvest. It was a relatively pleasant form of concentration camp, Namuth would recall. He played chess in the dappled light under the trees with his friend Andreas Becker, who was later arrested by the Vichy Government and returned to Germany. In order to escape repatriation after German forces occupied France, Namuth joined the Foreign Legion in 1940, where he served out his basic training in Morocco. When the war in Tunisia ended he fled to Marseille, spending the winter seeking assistance from Varian Fry's Emergency Rescue Committee which offered help to hundreds of Europeans –

including Hannah Arendt, André Breton, Marcel Duchamp and Max Ernst – to secure transportation to the United States. Just how Namuth was able to jump the queue, as it were, and be on one of the first transports out of Marseille is unknown. But in February 1941 he sold his cameras to pay for the crossing and, by way of Casablanca, arrived in New York City on 10th April 1941.

Hans Namuth was standing on Lexington Street halfway between the post office and the statue of Mercury high over the Tiffany Glass Clock of Grand Central Station when he received a telegram telling him that Georg Reisner, who had also fled in the direction of Marseille, where he allowed himself to imagine once more the islands and the light, had been arrested as he stepped onto the platform of the Marseille Saint Charles; he was incarcerated along with other German and Austrian traitors to the Reich, and sent to the dreaded Camp des Milles where, on Christmas Day, too afraid to go on, Reisner hanged himself in his cell. Namuth was inconsolable. During his first few months in America his health deteriorated and he decided, as if as a last resort, to look up distant relatives. In the days before he departed New York it rained continuously and as Namuth's train crossed the floodplains in the early light he looked out at the arable fields that once stretched as far as the eye could see. Now there was nothing but water, a flat grey mirror reflecting the sky and the crows, innumerable and lost, circling over it looking for somewhere to land.

At this point in his story, the journalist writes, Namuth appeared increasingly withdrawn as if he was sinking into himself, and several times he had to pause before forcing

himself on. Here Hans Namuth reminded me most of myself
– how hard it was I remember thinking to replace what had
happened with the emptiness of stories. And I remembered
again that inability to speak when asked by loved ones or
professionals, that inability to describe what I could not
understand. Namuth's story – the shadows, the unknown
turns, the lost chapters, the invisibility at the heart of his
photographs, seemed to come from an equivalent place, a
place I knew well.

What I remember most from that time in America, he said, *a
country which seemed to me then to be as wide as it was empty,
are my dreams. In one dream, Georg Reisner is standing on the
porch of an American colonial era homestead. It is evening.
Black rain clouds are gathering over the hills. I approach the
house and climb the first of the steps to the porch. Before I reach
the top the screen door opens and I am frozen in my tracks.
Reisner, pale and thin, glances at the darkening sky. Some men
walk into storms he tells his landlady who has come to see where
he is. Others walk with the storm always at their back.*

The sudden downpour drives them inside where his
landlady discovers Reisner passed out in Andre Malraux's
hotel room in Valencia, lent to Namuth in October 1936 by
the French author who would later invent a museum without
walls. The rainstorm has closed the roads down from the
mountains. Nobody will be able to leave for at least another
week. *I am trapped in that room,* Namuth writes. Whenever
Namuth woke from these dreams he was near suicidal. As
with every survivor, there is the question of why it was you
that should survive. Namuth moved from job to job living in
towns across the Mid-West.

There is no longer any doubt, he wrote in his diary in early 1942: *I am not disappointed by America. I am deeply shocked. I am paralysed like someone who has expected the Promised Land and found himself in the coldness of the desert. And I cannot discuss this with anybody. I must be* grateful *and fake it. Anybody who asked me (and everybody does ask)* How do you like America? *would feel personally insulted if my spontaneous reply would be anything but* Very much, very much indeed.

In January 1943, sleepless, in despair and racked by guilt, Namuth made his escape once more, this time into the ranks of the United States Military Intelligence Agency. At the end of that year, after receiving basic training, he sailed to Scotland on the Queen Mary and, a few days after D-Day, he landed on Omaha Beach before moving on to the Elbe and then Czechoslovakia. It is not clear what his duties consisted of until the War ended and he was assigned to the war crimes division in Freising in Germany where he travelled the British and American zones arresting wanted Germans. Namuth was demobilised on October 27, 1945. He did not return to Germany until after both his parents were dead, in the winter of 1970.

Back in America, Namuth was like a man wandering in a derelict town. Namuth had taken up photography once more but this time he worked alone. Holding a camera had ceased to feel natural to Hans Namuth, like he was toying with forces he didn't understand. *In my best portraits from that time*, he told the journalist, *the men and women I photographed appear whole – if only for an instant – even though I felt as if I had torn part of them away from themselves.* His new wife, Carmen Elisa Herrera, managed to secure him a job working for a company developing a patent for waterproof paper, but when the business went bust the following year, she and Hans travelled to her family's estate in Guatemala.

In the green light of the hills life seemed once again open and free. Through Herrera he met Maud Oakes, an anthropologist from California. One night over dinner Oakes asked him if he would assist her in photographing the people of Todos Santos, the Mam Indians, descendants of an ancient Mayan civilisation, who had lived for hundreds of years high in the Cuchamtan hills. Inaccessible by motorcar, the village was an eight-hour trek on horseback via steep tracks to the Paquix plateau and then down into the canyon of the Rio Chanjón. Few Europeans had spent any time in their midst. Namuth agreed.

Two weeks later, on descending the valley trail for the first time, Namuth photographed a shepherd climbing the slopes with his sheep. Namuth had acted on instinct but in an agonised voice the shepherd cried out, *What have you done to me?*

It was as if I had stuck a knife into him, Namuth said. Maud Oakes had been living in Todos Santos for over a year, studying the lives of this remote and ancient tribe, and needed a photographer to help illustrate the book she was writing, *The Two Crosses of Todos Santos.* No easy task. Even if what he found captivated Namuth, the men and women of the village refused to have their picture taken. When they saw Oakes with a camera they accused her of sorcery. Namuth had more success, but not until he had established a

41

relationship with individual elders would they permit him to take theirs or anybody else's picture and even then they acquiesced with some reluctance. Namuth occupied himself by photographing the surrounding landscape as if the world around him remained unreal until he looked at it through a lens. *I seem to be in several places at once*, he told the journalist, remembering the day he established a temporary darkroom in the bush. At night, Namuth listened intently to the coyotes in the hills, as under his hands each image from the day slowly resolved into light and shadow, forms and space. *Sound in the Cuchamtan Valley*, Namuth writes, *does not emanate from the jungle itself, or so it seems to me, but from within my own body. So much so that it is impossible to distinguish the calls of birds and animals, of the wind in the trees from one's thoughts. But the pictures – the images that we are taking away*, he continues, *bear no relation. It is not that they come from elsewhere, products of an alien invader, but that each one is an elsewhere: a forged memory of something that never took place. Being in this place*, he told Oakes one evening after several glasses of mescal, *is like attempting to write about mirrors – you know what they are and how they function but still there is something about them one can never understand.*

Twenty years later Maud Oakes would return to Central America only to be involved in a car accident of her own. Driving into the hills high over Lima she would find herself in the pitch dark following a truck through a rainstorm without headlights, her only guide the single red taillight of the truck ahead. She describes the mountain road giving way and the car slipping uncontrollably into a ravine followed by the terrible sensation of tumbling through black space. The car fell for more than a hundred feet but miraculously she and her passenger survived. For a long time I kept this picture of Maud Oakes by my desk taken by Namuth in Todos Santos in 1947, sitting astride her horse, like a rider of the light stationed at the gateway between one world and the next.

When the rains came, Namuth set up a large tent made of thick white canvas to make his portraits. In these images the electric lights chase away any shadows, any depth or ambiguity, so that the faces and bodies of Namuth's subjects seem to hang in mid air, as if they have appeared out of a fog into a world that is not their own. *When a photographer says*

Hold it, *and clicks the shutter,* Namuth told the journalist who interviewed him many years later, *he has imprisoned part of the person in his little black box. Primitive people know this and resent it,* he continues. *The Indians of Guatemala, with whom I spent much time, believe that the photographer is whisking away their very souls, and that they have to come back to retrieve them after they die.*

One night a violent storm blew through the camp, flattening huts and sending debris into the bush that flanked the hillside. Namuth's tent had been turned upside down. For several days villagers came across half developed contact sheets caught between fence posts and tree branches, in puddles, pig pens, grass banks and the timbers of outhouses far and wide across the rambling settlement that made up Todos Santos. These scattered fragments of his work seemed to mark out an enclosure from which there was no way out. By a strange twist of fate this picture of the house of a

shaman, Namuth had taken on arriving in Todos Santos, was found in the entranceway of the same building. The place seemed to be changing places with his pictures and the discovery struck him as an ill omen. *My grasp of what was real was slipping*, Namuth said. He quickly concluded his work with Oakes and, in the spring of 1947, he and Herrera returned to New York.

On his return to America the nightmares that had plagued him abated and Namuth could not believe how easy it was to take photographs again. While picking up regular advertising work with fashion magazines, he began taking classes with Alexey Brodovitch and in the summer of 1950, he was hired to photograph the painter Jackson Pollock. It was Brodovitch who convinced Namuth that Pollock was a significant artist and an excellent subject for a photographer embarking on a new career. When he saw Pollock's paintings on display, Namuth was far from captivated. He nonetheless trusted the judgement of his teacher, and the following July travelled to Pollock's studio on Long Island. On meeting, the two men were ill at ease. Pollock insisted he had finished for the day. He appeared to show the same suspicion of the camera that the Guatemalan tribal elders had shown, fearful perhaps of how much would be taken away. But he soon returned to the canvas laid out on the floor and, for less than an hour, Namuth photographed the painter as he worked.

Pollock and Lee Krasner liked a number of the images Namuth showed them the following weekend and from July until early October Namuth returned each week taking over 500 photographs of Pollock pouring, dripping and throwing paint. During the period immediately before Namuth's visits to Fireplace Road, Pollock was sober and producing large canvases the likes of which nobody had ever seen. Clement Greenberg called him America's greatest living painter. Frank O'Hara described Pollock's works from this time as *painfully beautiful celebrations of what will disappear, or has disappeared, of what may be destroyed at any moment.* But it was Namuth's photographs, published in Life the following year that transported Pollock into the abyss of absolute fame. *He became a sex symbol,* Namuth joked with the journalist. *Like Jayne Mansfield or James Dean!* Everyone thought of him as the very embodiment of lost authenticity, the journalist would write. Yet, in the summer of 1950, stopping and starting according to his directions, re-performing certain actions, pausing for the camera, it was Pollock who worked largely under the instruction of Namuth as if the painter had become an actor impersonating himself.

On the final night of Namuth's stay, Lee Krasner organised a dinner at the studio for Namuth and a small group of friends. Pollock stormed into the room, seemingly intoxicated. He repeatedly accused Namuth of being a phoney. At the end of the meal before Krasner could serve coffee, Pollock threw over the dinner table and left. Except for a brief spell at the end of 1952-3 Pollock produced little significant work. After 1954 he hardly painted at all. On the evening of August 11th 1956 he drove to meet his lover, Ruth Kligman, from the train. Kligman had travelled from Manhattan with a friend, Edith Metzger, whom she hoped would impress the famous painter. Pollock had been drinking all day and drove them to a bar where he and Kligman had a fight. Lets go home she said, Kligman wrote in an article many years later. She didn't want a drink. Pollock finished his beer and led them out.

On the road, Pollock refused to slow down, pushing the car harder and harder until, on a road approaching East Hampton, he lost control of the Oldsmobile and collided with a tree. Kligman woke unable to move. A crowd had gathered and a policeman told her none of her party had survived. Kligman didn't believe him. She asked a girl standing nearby if it was true. The girl, who was no more than seven years of age, went over to where the bodies were lying. She came back and told her it was okay. They were fine. Kligman looked at the girl and she knew that they were dead. As the journalist points out in his story: the fact Pollock's sobriety (and his most prolific period) ended on the very day Namuth finished photographing him is highly suggestive. Yet it's not clear if the journalist asked Namuth if he felt any remorse for what happened to Jackson Pollock. If he did, the question wasn't included in the published text.

As I fought to keep a grip on my notes and the diversions and displacements of Namuth's life, its myriad blind-spots smoothed out under the journalist's steady hand, it was Edith Metzger's disappearance that troubled me most. I hunted for many weeks for a picture of Edith Metzger but as far as I can discover, not a single image of the woman killed in Pollock's car survives. Metzger entered history on the same day that she departed almost without trace. How was it possible to enter this world of picture making and remain unseen I wondered? But then this experience may be more common than one might expect: there were only the few pictures we had kept, and a hospital ultrasound, of a child who entered the world on the same day that she left. There was, after all, a great deal Namuth could not recall. Pollock was not the first painter that he had photographed but Namuth could not remember which artist he had photographed before he took those pictures of Pollock. He did not keep records and those papers he had kept had either been lost or destroyed. *I do recall the trepidation*, Namuth told the journalist. At that point, I looked about me and wondered why I had taken it upon myself to amass all of these notes – to make up for these blank spots in what was know – to make up for what had been lost? Why, unlike Namuth, had I clung to what was left and pushed everything else away? I imagined being ransacked, I imagined a great storm coming and washing it all away, all the words, all the pictures, I imagined an inferno burning it down but none of it came close to the pain already installed in my heart.

After buying a house in East Hampton, not far from the Pollocks, Namuth, as charming and outgoing as ever, embarked on an extraordinary career. De Kooning, Albers, Hopper, Beuys, Calder, Dine, Rauschenberg, Johns, Deibenkorn, Martin, Newman, Reinhardt, Rivers, Rothko, Smith, Still, Hockney, Rosenquist, Segal, Steinberg, Kline, Kelly, Graves – all posed for Namuth's camera. According to those who knew him, Namuth's deep identification with the artists he photographed was testament to his skill and generosity. Yet, reading the cold detachment of his interview in 1980, I can't help wondering whether the associations he made with the lives of those he recorded in static images was, in fact, a result of the same separation he had felt in Paris in the 1930s and then in America after the war; whether no matter how hard he tried, Hans Namuth could never connect.

Having pursued him for many years, Namuth sent a postcard of Diane de Poitiers by Francois Clouet to the famously reclusive Joseph Cornell, hoping to take his picture. *Time goes and goes*, he writes. *Will we ever meet? I think of you*

(as of everything these days) with sadness in my heart.
Namuth may as well have been reaching into a mist and yet,
eventually, in 1971, Cornell granted him his wish.

The resulting image has haunted me for many years.
Whom did Namuth meet on that lonely shore other than a
stranger attempting to pass as quickly as possible, seeing
nobody, as if nobody was there. I realised then it is not
Cornell that we see but Namuth. As in all of his pictures,
Namuth became invisible so as to be more present in what
was gone as if his sole melancholic purpose in photographing
so many of the most influential painters of the time was to
manufacture a set of hiding places into which he could
disappear; to tell his own bizarre and restless story precisely
by not telling it. This was one part of his life I could at least
understand. For a long time I had been under the impression
that this image, taken by Maud Oakes sometime after the
storm destroyed Namuth's tent in Guatemala, showed the
German at work in a replacement darkroom built for him by

local craftsmen using hardier materials than the previous canvas and rope. But my copy of the photograph is in fact a picture of Marcel Griaule, who in 1946 as holder of the Sorbonne's first chair in ethnology, would lecture in his air force officer's uniform. With this mistaken identity, Namuth's invisibility appeared, to me at least, complete. Yet Namuth must have known that the photographer, like all anthropologists, participates in the world he wipes out.

On Saturday October 13th, 1990, *Take an Object* premiered in New York. In the film, Jasper Johns was working on his new paintings. In a quiet moment, the presenter asks Johns what it is like to be photographed by Hans Namuth. Johns shrugs. *He asks me to repeat myself sometimes*, he said. *But mostly it was as if he wasn't there.* One of the pictures he is painting shows a pair of arms reaching into unfathomable depths. *That's Hart Crane*, says Johns, diving into the Caribbean Sea. As the film rolls on, however, I can't help wondering whether Johns was telling the truth. Is that Crane, I thought, or could it be Namuth disappearing beneath his own reflecting pool one that didn't show him back to himself except in the eyes of other people. Namuth left the premier before the end. By midnight he reached the Hamptons. There was no rain. It is not clear if Namuth was speeding or if he ran a junction but at 12.06 am his car collided with another vehicle and he was killed instantly on a country road not far from where Jackson Pollock lost his life.

5

In 1961, Jackson Pollock's close friend, Tony Smith, was nearly killed in a car accident in upstate New York. Smith had been commissioned to design a house for the art dealer Betty Parsons (who organised the exhibition of Pollock's work Hans Namuth had seen before he photographed Pollock in 1951) and was on his way to visit the site when his station wagon collided with a lorry just outside of Albany. Ten years in the making, the house was never built, although a number of small scale maquettes exist as well as many more photographs of models that show different versions of the possible home.

After working with Frank Lloyd Wright in the 1930s, Smith had established his own practice, designing experimental houses based on modular units that could fit together in ever-expanding patterns. But in the months after the accident that left him with on-going pain and a debilitating blood condition which, twenty years later, would eventually take his life, he turned to designing purely abstract objects for which he had no real name. They are neither architecture nor sculpture – *I think of them as presences* he once told an art critic and it's true: the large black objects, most of them larger than a human being, seem to have been cut out of the air around them, like shapes left by something that has gone. *I call them art*, he said, *only because that is a term people seem to understand*. The Elevenses Are Up, his first exhibited sculpture and one that only ever existed as a plywood mock up, was destroyed soon after being displayed in 1963.

I often wonder if Smith's peculiar works ever actually existed. I for one have only seen Smith's sculptures in photographs or, should I say, reproductions of photographs either taken by him or people he knew published in magazines and catalogues of which I have kept a number of copies. After I moved away so that Anne could be alone, I sometimes would spread these pictures around my room and laid out in this way, randomly, without any obvious connection except where they happen to fall, they began to look like studies for a potential architecture, one without rooms. Rooms like the one I was working in, I noted at the time, or the rooms we are forever moving between. In fact, an architecture (if that's the right word) where there are no interiors at all, only a

Amaryllis, plywood mockup, 11'6" x 7'6" x 11'6", (to be shown in Hartford).

repeating view on the same external façade. These surfaces, like certain forms of dream, stand in, as one might say, for a set of missing interiors that change even though they are gone only because we restlessly alter our position in relation to where they happen to be standing and because we believe they are solid even though we know – if one is being honest – that they could just as easily disappear altogether.

In 1966 Smith attempted to describe the way he worked, often putting his objects together by chance. The final configuration for this piece named Willy after a character in a play by Samuel Beckett, came to him in the moments between sleep and wakefulness. *I had the piece built out of plywood and weather proofed with black car undercoating,* he told Sam Wagstaff. *On seeing it in the garden, my friend said it looked like somebody who can't get off the ground. I*

told him that they are first shapes. They are there before I am. That must be why I originally encounter them, before I have even drawn a line, when I am caught halfway between sleep and consciousness – neither in one place or the other, as if it is only between states that anything lasting or meaningful can come into form.

It's in this way that I often think of the house Smith failed to build for Parsons as a kind of dream house, not of the kind we are sold on television and in magazines, but the kind of house we inhabit when we meet one another under completely different circumstances, when we suddenly find ourselves as though inhabiting the dreams of other people.

Not long after the car accident Smith woke one morning in great pain, unable to move. *For some time I could not call to anyone,* he said, *and I found myself staring at a glass pitcher of water on a bedside table. The water had been left standing all night and a constellation of many tiny bubbles hung motionless in the jug. Each tiny bead was perfectly empty he remembers thinking and the glass pitcher was suddenly nothing but an outline – a drawing in mid air. Yet this near invisible scene looked heavy and solid compared with anything else in the room. I could not think of volume in the same way again, he recalled.* That is to say: without thinking of pain and weightlessness – of something so empty it is full.

When Tony Smith was four years old he contracted tuberculosis and was quarantined to a garden room behind his family's home where he spent a summer and an autumn separated from his parents and siblings. In the evenings, to help him sleep, his mother and father would take turns reading Jules Verne through the door. To pass time during the day he began to build shapes from the used medicine packets left in the room by his doctor, who soon realised the young Smith was far more interested in these empty containers than in the actual playthings he had been furnished with. By opening the cartons and folding them in certain ways, Smith discovered he could link up any number of them and create high towers or sprawling castles or forts. For many hours he worked this way, learning about the integral strength of even the flimsiest material, and that things could connect endlessly even if those connections were made randomly without forethought or planning but based solely on the immediate pleasure of putting one thing next to another.

In the years after his bout of tuberculosis, emptiness and

the stories of adventure Smith had loved throughout his youth combined. In the early 1950s, ten years before his car accident, a colleague at Cooper Union where Smith had been teaching architecture, told him of an unfinished highway linking Jersey City with The Bronx. One night Smith took three students there in his car. As they left the lighted road and drove up onto the Turnpike there were no lights or shoulder markers, lines, railings or anything at all except the dark pavement moving through the landscape of the flats, rimmed by hills in the distance, punctuated by stacks, towers, fumes and colored lights. They drove in silence, aware they were looking for something but unsure what it might be. *I thought to myself, it ought to be clear that's the end of art, Smith recalls. Most paintings look pretty pictorial after that. Later, says Smith, I discovered a number of abandoned airstrips in Europe – these deserted landscapes had nothing to do with any function – created worlds without tradition. There is a drill ground in Nuremberg, large enough to accommodate two million men. The entire field is enclosed with high embankments and towers. The concrete approach is three 16-inch steps, one above the other, stretching for a mile or so.* Looking back, I think Smith realized, recalling a scene from ten years before by which time his world in the making had changed immeasurably, that what he was looking for would always be out of reach. He was seeking an immediate present that seemed only to exist in ghost stories, like his night drive on an unfinished road straight out of the books he'd gone to sleep listening to as a child born into a world where he would always be alone making what he could of the empty objects he was surrounded by.

During those weeks and months, as I worked through the documents relating to Tony Smith and the other victims of car accidents, it became increasingly difficult to sleep. Many nights would go by as I lay in the dark waiting for dawn. Living as I did back then, away from Anne on the outskirts of a vast city, I often wondered how many others suffered the same fate: each of us lying in black boxes, staring at nothing hoping that somehow we would drift away from the torment of our waking thoughts. What is a room, I remember thinking while drifting through the night, except a place where people dream or cry or disappear? Thinking this way, Smith's black geometric forms began to look like so many over-sized monuments to the cubes we surround ourselves with. They could be doorways or beds, I thought, houses or coffins, or books. Yet Smith, who struggled throughout his life with insomnia, made his prototypes not as lasting monuments but in order to see his ideas appear briefly outside of his mind, as it were, within the world where he had to live like everybody else. Most of these prototypes were destroyed and the majority of them were only realised as completed works – made from galvanised steel and other more permanent materials – after Smith's death in 1980. Indeed, the impressive series of prototypes that he produced during this frenetic period after the crash were largely made in order to be photographed; so much so that the three dimensional forms that could be one thing and then another depending on the direction of one's approach were flattened into two dimensions – fixed in appearance – and were from then on no bigger than a diagram in a work manual. The sculptures – if that's what they are – seem to float in the centre of a strange white space without reference to any particular place or time. Take for instance the original cover of Lucy Lippard's book *Tony Smith*. It shows *Gracehopper*, the dimension, scale and even brute size of which are all but erased from the picture – it could be a model standing on a white tabletop or it could be the size of a house. Either way we have to keep our distance if we hope to see what it is. But these peculiar human-sized objects constructed in order to be photographed before the things themselves are obliterated can only have been made, it seems to me, in order to haunt a time of fabrication, a time you might come upon quite by accident, like a line in a book or something you heard someone say as they were passing in the street, pulling you up short so that for a moment it seems you have forgotten where you are or where you have been, or, for that matter, where you thought you were going. But it was not Smith's missing sculptures that were important to me then and which held sleep at arm's length. It was the black square shapes of what had remained unborn, of what could not be recovered in any memory of a single person's life.

In a portrait Hans Namuth made for the cover of Art News in 1971, Tony Smith is dwarfed by one of his objects, which on first glance reminded me of a giant capital *I*. Compared with the paintings of his friend Jackson Pollock, where being in the painting was the same as being inside himself, Smith assumed an outwardness when he came to make his work. His was a landscape seen from a distance, but one that always appeared to be near at hand. If it did show an interior it would be one where the occupants had just left; they may be back any moment or they may never return home. It's odd to see Smith standing there like that, in front of that giant *I* as if in fact he is standing in front of himself: as if all he can do is cancel himself out. Looking at that picture, it seemed to me that Smith did not look for himself inwardly. His was not the self as a kind of privatized pastime, but one only in existence (if at all), beyond the boundaries of the individual; an identity fragmented across any number of versions of its own appearance – adrift, as it were, in a field of infinitely reproducible photocopies – lost, strange and displaced. I thought again of Smith's story of his drive through a landscape that no longer exists and I wondered if it were not the case that all stories involve a kind of wiping out of the events they report. But of course, I remember thinking: that is what makes each story so hard to be without.

Given my lack of sleep, there were periods when my endless note-taking and the copies of the pictures I was surrounding myself with started to merge with the reality of everyday events so that at times I wondered if I were awake or if I had finally succumbed to a state of rest; even if it was one filled with dreams so vivid they could have amounted to the sum parts of a waking life; a life that was not my own necessarily but one belonging to somebody who could just as likely have been myself. I soon realised the only way I could live in my room, far from everything I loved, was to take a photograph and to inhabit the room that way.

Over time, I cleared away the reproductions of works by Tony Smith and the other images I was trying to put into order, and lined the walls, instead, with photographs showing the room from different angles and at different times. Sometimes it was night. In other pictures the sun was coming up and the writing table, chair and the edge of the bed appear to be caught in an uncertain light as if the objects I saw every day were in fact apparitions.

One night, in something of a panic I tore down the photographs and returned to my notes, emptying onto the floor a folder marked Boxes. Out fell any number of reproductions from that same elusive period in history – a period made all the more elusive by the weight of writing describing its events – when so many artists, say during the two decades after 1955, set about the task of building box after box. Scattered across the floor the pictures looked like evidence collected from some distant land in the grip of a dreadful civil war where the demand for coffins was high. Some of these boxes were large, like Smith's *Die*, close in size to the dimensions of a grown man, while others, such as Robert Morris's *Box with the sound of its own making*, were much smaller, closer in size to a newborn child. (In the picture I have of Morris's Box, in which he concealed a playable three-hour sound recording made on the morning he cut and joined the pieces of his wooden cube, the box takes on the shape of a silent space in the middle of the page surrounded by so many printed words). According to my notes, there are four versions of Tony Smith's sculpture, *Die*, two of which were fabricated after his death in 1980 (the same year as Barthes' fatal car accident). The two versions made during Smith's lifetime are held in the Whitney Museum of Art in New York and America's National Gallery in Washington DC. The dimensions of the work – six foot-by six foot-by six foot – along with its strange history of re-fabrication either side of Smith's death, mean that comparisons with the tomb are almost unavoidable. And yet, the original six-inch cardboard model, made in 1962 and which no longer exists (the first full-sized steel version wasn't made until some years later – some say 1968 although Robert Morris describes seeing it in 1966), is said to be based on a card index file. It appears remarkable to me that such an iconic piece of American sculpture, neither an object (too big for that) nor a monument (too small), should be based on a box of notes meant to organize a world in writing, one pieced together from fragments that may or may not relate.

6

The year John Latham exhibited the car in which he was very nearly killed was also the year of Robert Morris's first major exhibition in Britain. As the finishing touches were being made to what was intended to be a survey of the minimalist cubes and rhomboids for which the American was best known, Morris decided to scrap the whole show and replace it with a set of works based on a rough cardboard model made in his studio. Weights on ropes, ramps, sandbags, a large wooden ball, a concrete cylinder big enough for walking in, a tightrope and a balancing beam, tunnels, climbing slots and climbing chimneys were all set up as part of what would look unnervingly like an assault course or playground arranged across the grand halls of the Duveen Galleries at the Tate, in the spring of 1971. The only instructions for how to use the odd assemblage of play-things were photographs pinned to the walls close to each exhibit showing people awkwardly balancing, scaling, or crawling on the shapes.

Sadly it took just five days for the gallery to decide that the show could not stay open. After a number of minor accidents and damage to the works caused by what one curator described as the *exuberant and excited* behaviour of some visitors, the exhibition was closed, the playground was swept away, and the show re-opened less than a week later in

the form of a more traditional career survey. It must have been strange for anyone attending the second attempt at Morris's "retrospective" knowing that it was a kind of stand-in for the real exhibition all but erased by the organisers at Tate. The only references that remained were the mocked up instructional photographs, made with the help of museum staff and later included in a revised catalogue. I love looking at these photographs, and feel some sympathy for the awkwardness of those employed, as it were, to test out the exhibits – the attendants seem unsure either how to do so or quite why they should. It's as if, the photographs seem to say, real life has at last been allowed to begin; then, just as the scene gets under way, it has to be stopped as abruptly as it began. I don't know if it is merely this sense of lost time, but the people in those pictures look strangely frozen, drained of the physical or sensual qualities associated with the body in motion. Instead they appear disoriented like someone picking through the rubble of a house destroyed in the night. They don't quite know how to perform their role, and I suppose this is what I like about them. Or it could be because they seem to be acting out our inability to remember and our near frenzied organisational impulse to fill those gaps in memory, those blank spaces that come to stand for things we know to be true but can neither feel, see, hear or touch directly.

While researching what seemed to be moments increasingly out of reach, so many of them pictured in their making as something that could only disappear, I could not shake the impression that the photographs from the erased Morris exhibition had something to do with aerial views of post-war London I had once seen in a book. I remember staring at the pictures as a child for some time before realising to my horror that what I had assumed were smudged thumbprints were in fact whole blocks of buildings flattened by bombs, many close to the streets where I had grown up. By the time I was old enough to notice, most of these sites had been built over with mass-housing projects.

Many of these gaps in the urban landscape would have still been in evidence in 1966, however, when young men and women across the world gathered in London to destroy, once and for all, what their parent's generation referred to as *art*. The evidence is patchy but there are reports in magazines from the time documenting what John Latham and his friend Gustav Metzger, an exiled orphan of the Second World War, described as a *Symposium*, on art and destruction. My first notes on the ramshackle array of improvised dances, film screenings and public meetings refer to a destruction *of* art symposium. For whatever reason, this misreading has stuck with me as I tried for weeks on end to discover what it was exactly Latham and his friends were attempting to wipe away.

A bombsite behind Notting Hill Gate was renamed the London Free School Playground, reminding me of the Tate gallery attendants attempting to balance on boards and balls. It was here that large abstract paintings were burned while Al Hansen drove a motorbike into a wall. Latham incinerated stacks of books outside the British Museum as Metzger melted nylon canvases with acid. Above all, however, I was struck by reports of a work no longer in existence made by Barry Flanagan while he was still John Latham's student at Saint Martins School of Art. A pile of sand about a meter square was positioned in the central aisle of the Mercury Theatre, in Ladbroke Grove, where the final evening of The Destruction in Art Symposium was taking place. The neat square wasn't roped off in any way and over the course of the night most of the people who happened to be there would have walked through the work spreading sand around the space, inadvertently turning one thing into another. By the end of the evening, the melancholic work was both everywhere and nowhere at once. I have no idea what Flanagan must have thought about his work but the displaced, even obliterated sculpture strikes me as symptomatic of a moment that may have been the end or the beginning of a time that is all but lost.

Just as the final events were taking place, of which only titles survive, including Anthony Cox's *Sword Piece*, Yoko Ono's *Disappearing Piece,* and what is described in dog-eared programme notes as a *Silent Explosion* by Ivor Davies, Flanagan's work was being turned into a strange form of nothingness, as if, playing amid the ruins, real life at last begins.

Looking down on the scraps of text and the murky copies of photographs from that September in London the evidence starts to look more and more like a map, one made of missing streets, of districts abandoned to the distortions of time. Much of what happened in 1966 took place in a rundown bookshop close to Cecil Court. The shop was managed by Bob Cobbing, a poet and musician, whose strange typewritten texts are the closest thing I have to a blueprint for the invisible city of that time. At one point, as actors with pickaxes and shovels dug out the very foundations of the shop, the basement was all but demolished. Part dream, part history, I imagine the room, buried as it were beneath upper chambers stuffed with books and papers, to be more like a waiting area at the end of an empty railway platform or a storeroom for some peculiar factory of texts.

Later that year, as the dust settled, Cobbing and his friends set up a filmmaker's cooperative in the same room beneath the bookshop. It seems fitting that the void left by art's would-be destruction was suddenly populated by flickering shadows as if nothing could exist in the space left behind but the recordings of other times and places, of what is both with us and is gone; a ghost-world.

7

I continued to sleep badly, woken most nights by the dream of a tree burning in a field beside a lake. Disturbed, but unable to turn away, I would wake exhausted having only just fallen asleep. I hadn't thought about the dream in waking life until I visited a cinema in Milan and watched once more Pasolini's Gospel According to Saint Matthew. I had travelled to the city, in view of the Alps rising out of the ground like a line of ghosts marching grimly into the distance, to meet with L., a professor of film who, unaware of what had happened in my life, had written to me out of the blue and asked if I would speak with her students. Ordinarily I would have declined but I was glad of the distraction and in many ways had all but given myself up then to the whims of work and other people. But when I arrived at the Hotel Milanese a message had been left telling me that tomorrow's seminar had been cancelled. A fire had started two nights before in a basement lab for developing student films. It quickly spread to the library above. Miraculously no one was hurt but the library's entire collection was lost in the flames. In the resulting chaos L. had neglected to tell me that there was no need to travel to Milan.

I looked around the lobby of the hotel. It was shabby and dark but the thought of leaving the city and returning to London there and then was exhausting. I left my bag with the clerk and walked out into the heat. Disburdened suddenly of all obligation I strolled aimlessly for several hours, stopping only once to eat at the Pizzeria Verona, until I came upon the Cinema Elizio, which was showing a selection of works by Pier Paolo Pasolini. I bought a ticket and sat down in the air-conditioned dark just as his Gospel film was starting. Exhausted after walking the streets of a city I didn't know, I must have fallen asleep, only to wake quite suddenly at the scene in which Christ, hungry and angered that the plant bears no fruit, curses a fig tree. How quickly it withers, Judas observes, as the camera cuts back to the same black branches dividing the same white sky, only now distorted; twisted into the outlines of death. My dream of the burning tree combined in my mind with the burned library I would never visit, as if it had been dreamt by somebody else; for a time I couldn't remember where I was or how I had got there.

When the film ended I resumed my journey through the same streets, convinced that many years had passed even

though I had gone that way only an hour or so before. How easy it is, I began to think, for these flickering half-images, these apparitions, to connect things in places and times that have nothing to do with one another. How many missed images must we live with only to encounter them in films or dreams?

Pasolini made the film in 1964, and its cast, made up of poets, intellectuals, family members and truck drivers, included a young Gorgio Agamben, who played the role of Filipo, one of Christ's disciples, a decade before Agamben would become more widely known as a modern philosopher and whose books would be published around the world to great acclaim. A figure in the background, Filipo is all but silent in the film. He repeats only a single line uttered by each of the disciples at the last supper when Christ announces one of the twelve will betray him: *Lord, is it I?* At one point he can be seen, no more than a teenager, distributing bread and fish on the shores of Galilee, and I began to wonder what it was that could link this youthful figure, pursuing, one must

assume, some form of career in the Italian film industry with his later incarnation. Of course the two people are not the same, not in any complete sense: the young man in the background who comes into close-up only a handful of times and who utters all but a few words, has disappeared, even as I can observe him here re-photographed for no real purpose. I doubt Giorgio Agamben recognises this Filipo except as Filipo and not as an image of himself.

I had been reading and attempting to understand his unfinished and fragmentary book on *the destruction of experience* when Anne and I were waiting for our second child to be born. When I started these notes the essay, seemed in my confusion more like another mourning diary than a philosophy book. Agamben described a world defined by numbness and separation, where things have no shape or value except for how they are reported, as abstractions without reference to what may or may not have taken place. It was a world I knew well and had been thrown into anew, cut off from the time before our trip to the hospital, before the silence invaded our home, before the fights and the screaming and before Anne sent me away for all our sakes.

From then on I could only recognise myself as a stranger, as someone I am not, as if I had bumped into myself on an unfamiliar street, apologised and continued on my way. I often wondered if this was what happened to all actors who in order to play their roles in a convincing manner have to move further and further away from themselves. Is this what happened to the young Gorgio, who had decided instinctively to abandon part of himself in that figment of the screen, as if Pasolini's Filippo existed, not as a character, but as a clearing in a wood at the end of a complex set of pathways that never connect?

Pasolini died in 1975. As with Roland Barthes, Isadora Duncan and Jackson Pollock, his death involved an automobile. In the early hours of Nov 2, Pasolini's body was found in the middle of a recreation ground on the outskirts of Rome. He had been badly beaten and run over several times with his own car. A 17 year-old rent boy, who was arrested for stealing Passolini's Alfa Romeo, later confessed to the murder. Since my trip to Milan, so brief I can hardly be sure it happened, I have kept a large-scale reproduction of a photograph taken at Pasolini's funeral pinned to the wall beside my desk. Shot from somewhere above the procession, the image is filled almost to bursting with a sea of faces, as those in attendance crush around the passage of the casket through the streets of Rome.

I don't know if Agamben was also in attendance that day, but I'm sure it would have not been lost on him just how cinematic life could become, especially at that unaccountable moment. Indeed, whenever I thought about my own death, something that had begun to occupy me then, I was inevitably an onlooker, observing myself as if these things were not happening to me. I am told that this is the only way any of us can imagine death, as if the tools for doing so were taken away from us at birth, like a limb, or a relative, and replaced with a way of seeing ourselves we learn from going to the movies. If we have no other means to apprehend the dark that looms for all of us, how can any experience be but a separation from ourselves? Or is it that we can only imagine our own deaths through the deaths of other people; through

the images and fragmentary works they leave behind; in the shape of their disappearance – like watching over someone as they sleep? Scanning the faces at Pasolini's funeral, it seems to me that Pasolini was not inside the box being carried that day. It seems to me, that Pasolini was adrift, as if he could only exist, however partially and in however many fragments, in the disparate imaginations of those individuals of the crowd, that unidentified collection of lost souls.

It was during this period, when I could not sleep and had all but abandoned my research that I had, almost without realising it, started to keep a list of dead movie stars. It was the kind of activity, I now realised, that the shell-shocked undertake if only for the combined sense of horror and peace it invokes. On hearing that an actor or an actress had died, whether due to a car accident, drug overdose, or some so-called natural event, I would add a new name to the list. Such deaths were surprisingly frequent: it seemed to me that at least once a week there was a new obituary or announcement on the television. As time passed I began to include stars from the past (whose deaths I had, as it were, *missed*) as well as film directors, camera operators, script writers, even those who composed the music for films so that the list, typed down the centre of each page, began to form an endless column of text, one that reminded me of Constantine Brancusi's *Column Without End*.

I recently discovered a fragment of the list tucked into the pocket of an old coat. I must have wanted to keep it on my person during the winter months that followed our trip to the hospital. It included the name of Christopher Reeve. The irony was lost on no one when Superman was paralysed from

Hollis Frampton (1984), Henry Hathaway (1985), Frank Feylen (1985), Otto Preminger (1986), Andy Warhol (1987), Jack Smith (1988), John Cassavetes (1989), Salvador Dali (1989), Sergio Leone (1989), Jack Starrett (1989), Carl-Heinz Schroth (1989), Harry Smith (1991), Gregory Markopoulos (1992), Marjorie Keller (1993), Paul Sharits (1993), Donald Simpson (1996), Lucio Fulci (1996), King Hu (1997), Dawn Steel (1997), Juzol Hami (1997), Shirley Clarke (1997), Sheldon Leonard (1997), Fred Zinneman (1997), Adriana Caseloti (1997), James Broughton (1999), Stanley Kubrick (1999), Gail Fisher (2000), Jun Fukuda (2000), Leo Gordon (2000), Sidney Peterson (2000), Larry Buchanan (2004), Christopher Reeves (2004), Neal Fredericks (2004), Marlon Brando (2004), Ronald Bergan (2004), Ofelia Guilmain (2005)

the neck down after being thrown from a horse in 1995. I'm not sure why I kept the list. It seemed to serve as nothing more than a reminder that when I happened to glimpse any of these individuals in the cinema or in television re-runs late at night that I was only ever watching ghosts. But this is nothing new. In 1915, Luigi Pirandello, a writer connected to Filipo and Pasolini only by the country of their birth, told the story of Gubbio, a cameraman, driven to madness by his occupation on the film sets that made Milan the centre briefly of the cinema universe. *I am to them, in reality, a sort of executioner*, Gubbio writes in his diary. *My actors and actresses moving through their silent world feel as though they were in exile. Their action, the living action of their living bodies, there on the screen of the cinematograph, no longer exists: it is their image alone, caught in a moment, in a gesture, an expression, that flickers and disappears. They are confusedly aware, with a maddening, indefinable sense of emptiness, that their bodies are, so to speak, subtracted, suppressed, deprived of their reality, of breath, of voice, of the sound that they make in moving about, to become only a dumb image which quivers for a moment on the screen and disappears, in silence, in an instant, like an unsubstantial phantom, the play of illusion upon a dingy sheet of cloth.*

Any of us, it struck me in Milan as I walked back through the streets filled with traffic noise and the ceaseless movement of what suddenly appeared to me to be its achingly fashionable population, could have written Gubbio's diary. In fact, I think it must have come to me in my dreams, out of those grey lands that lie between what we know and how we know it. Indeed, reading over my notes, these strange chapters had begun to feel like a series of disappearances. I remember an artist whose work I admired a great deal saying something similar about her paintings. Where do they come from, she asked. From photographs? From dreams? From something someone said? In order to find out, I have to destroy two out of every three of the pictures I make. And I still do not know. But then so much of life is determined by that gravitational pull toward oblivion, toward finding out what, if anything, gets left behind. And of course there is always something, she said. The gnarled, burnt substance of what we can never bring ourselves to report.

8

In late 2013, before things fell apart, I learned that WG Sebald had been killed in a car accident in 2005. This came to me as something of a shock – not that he had died in this way but that the information had until now passed me by. I decided to drive with Anne and my then only daughter from London to Orford on the Suffolk coast. Autopsy reports showed Sebald had died of an aneurism moments before his car collided head-on with a lorry. His teenage daughter, who was at his side in the accident, was mercifully spared. Sebald was fifty-seven and on the brink of being awarded the Nobel Prize for literature.

Who am I? Andre Breton asks at the beginning of his novel *Nadja*. Perhaps, Breton suggests – setting out on an oneiric path through a series of recollections triggered and evidenced partially in grainy images like someone stunned by all they have seen and heard – everything would amount to knowing whom I haunt. Breton's novel reminds me of the way Sebald, who was born in the Alps but lived most of his adult life in the flatlands of East Anglia, was often described as a *ghostwriter*.

Making our way out of the city, in what seemed like broken stages of time as if the places going past our windows had been cut from discarded pieces of film, I thought as I often did when driving at speed, that we only come to discover the lives of other people when we collide. I had given no thought to what we would do in Orford and before I knew where we were I found myself in the 12th Century Castle Keep idly thinking of Robert Morris's erased play structures (made and then taken away in the year of John Latham's car accident), as my daughter (who was three years old at the time) and I moved up and down the central staircase built into the immensely thick southern wall trying to imagine what life would have been like for the original inhabitants. On our third or fourth circuit from the basement to the roof, a guide, clearly irked by our repetitive journey stopped to ask if we were aware of why the staircase spiraled upwards to the right. I said we hadn't noticed. The guide explained that if the castle walls and portcullis had been breached at ground level, the staircase being defended from the upper floors, offered predominantly right-handed swordsman fighting from above an advantage over those attempting to ascend.

Walking back into the village past where the original beacon had stood, I remembered that Roland Barthes had been left-handed. Later I would read somewhere that the French author's favourite shape in nature was the spiral; this had something to do with how the form described a continuous movement, along a line. One that would never pull too far from its beginning and would offer a kind of echo through the inherent proximity to itself within its upward climb and inevitable descent.

When Brancusi was asked to draw James Joyce for the cover of his book, Brancusi insisted that the two men meet. After several days in his company, Brancusi refused the

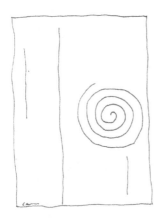

publisher's request. Instead he sent this drawing, which I traced into my notebook, to James Joyce and told him the figure of perpetual creation, the sacred spiral, the Sheela-na-gig, was the nearest he could come to a likeness of his new friend. I cannot be certain why I traced the drawing, following, as it were, Brancusi's hand: perhaps I had thought then, as I do now, that Nature, like God, arrived out of the dreams of people who are desperate and lost.

On our way from Orford we stopped in Walberswick. Anne looked at me as we parked. All day it had been difficult to speak. None of us knew why we were there and I soon found myself alone, close to the house where Humphrey Jennings was born, standing beneath a large elm, a survivor of the disease that wiped out so many of its kind in the 1960s. I set off along the road, turning almost immediately onto an overgrown footpath in the direction of the North Sea. I tracked behind a set of allotments and followed the path along a ridge of apparently endless cornfields. Eventually, the way led down into woods quickly opening onto the marshlands, which, for now at least, flank that stretch of the Suffolk coast. I had never visited this part of the British countryside and yet it felt oddly familiar as if I were following a route I had taken in my childhood, one that came back to me only in my dreams or at intervals when my thoughts were interrupted by events outside of my control.

Making my way through the head-high reeds and bulrushes, a white admiral flickering briefly in the light ahead, I passed the remains of a long abandoned wind pump. At some point I came to a crossing with a farm track raised above the reeds, which, after a few hundred yards, ran up against a high gate. I shrugged and turned around, mindful, suddenly, that I didn't have much time. Looking back it is not clear exactly what happened – it seems to me now that instead of retracing my steps I was walking in a direction opposite from the way I had come. Having found the path that dropped back down into the reeds I walked on, unaware that anything had changed until I found myself entering a different wood and the sandy track beneath my feet split into a series of forking paths.

I had taken a wrong turn and was making my way through the ancient forest on the edge of what I would later learn was Dunwich Heath. I remembered reading that once a walker had entered the web of tracks crisscrossing the heather and gauze, which were, at that time of year, chest high and more or less impenetrable, it was easy for them to lose their way. At one point I came upon two wooden arrows nailed to a post. If the way markers had at one time carried information as to where the paths might lead, this had long since weathered into a smooth blank so that the arrows now stood in mute mockery of the traveller. Having cut left and right and gone back on myself several times, I decided to choose a path and stick to it, the way one might navigate a maze. But this did not improve matters and after what felt like another hour I could observe, with growing despondency, the same lone tree on the horizon as if I were merely circling a central point to which I could get no closer nor could I get further away.

Automatically I felt through my pockets. Remarkably, the one thing in my possession was a drawing my daughter had made that morning of a spiral, having studied for some time the progress of a garden snail across the palm of her hand. She had already begun to forget that she was meant to have a sister. There was so much she did not know, I thought, and yet looking at her drawing – pointing to a different past and a different future – it seemed to me then that she knew more than anyone else.

I continued on my way. Perhaps because of the bending lines of flight that defined his writings, the form of the spiral, whenever I happened upon it, combined in my mind with the death of Villem Flusser in 1991 in a car accident close to the border of Germany and Czechoslovakia. Flusser was fond of recalling the shape of the spiral in order to explain the world around him, a world from which he felt increasingly disconnected. Words and pictures (or what he called lines and surfaces) had somehow become free of one another so that the present, he writes somewhere, does not look like the result of a linear development from image to memory, but rather like the result of a sort of spiral movement from image through memory to image. As I all but lost my balance at yet another fork in the path, grasping suddenly for a hold on reality, I began to recite a passage from memory, my lips silently mouthing each word as I stumbled on:

When man assumed himself subject of the world, when he stepped back from the world to think about it – when he became man – he did so mainly thanks to his curious capacity to imagine the world. Thus, he created a world of images to mediate between himself and the world of facts with which, because of this distance-taking process, he was beginning to lose contact. Later, he learned how to handle his imaginal world, thanks to another human capacity – the capacity to conceive. Through thinking in concepts, he became not only subject to an objectified world of facts, but also subject to an objectified world of images. Now, however, by again having recourse to his imaginal capacity, he is beginning to learn how to handle his conceptual world. Through imagination, he is now beginning to objectify concepts and thus to free himself from them. In the first instance, he stands in the midst of static images (in myth); in the second position, he stands in the midst of linear progressive concepts (in history); in the third position he stands in the midst of images that order concepts (in "structures").

The sun cut sideways across the gorse and my monologue, which, given the circumstances struck me as increasingly absurd, was interrupted by a loud bang framed in the still air by a piercing screech. I fixed on the sound, which may have come to me several months earlier, and moved as fast as the heather would allow in the direction of what must be, so I reasoned to myself, a road, and a way out of the maze. As I ran, one of Flusser's fondest examples began to play back in my fractured mind like a set of magic-lantern slides.

One night in 1912, Flusser's fellow Czech, Franz Kafka was driven into Munich in the rain. As the driver called their names, the great places that they passed – the Nymphenberg Palace, the Vier Jahreszeiten – were obscured by darkness and rainwater cascading on the screen, and each sight appeared to Kafka, instead, as vague lights and sounds; a journey he could only compare in his diaries, as the tyres of the carriage hummed on the wet asphalt, to a cinematographic film without images projected upon the wall of his mind. This odd recollection collided with a picture of Hans Zischler, the actor who appeared in the films of Wim Wenders and who, in later life, would write a book called Kafka at the Movies which he began to research late at night after long days on the sets of popular soap operas made for German television in the 1990s. As I crashed through the gorse I saw Zischler's Volkswagon Beetle fly through the air at full speed and smash into a river in the opening scene of *Kings of the Road*, a film I saw completely by accident a week or so earlier one wet night in London when I could not be at home.

Miraculously, the thicket, now densely packed and growing above my head so that I felt as if I were passing through a mesh, gave way and I found myself at the edge of an empty road. I looked one way and then the other expecting to find the remains of a hideous collision; but there was nothing. I sat down in a layby to catch my breath. More alone than ever, I listened to the yellowhammers at work in the hedgerows and felt calm for the first time in weeks. I am not sure how long I rested at the side of the road but not a single car passed by.

As the day grew dark I stood and followed the road back into Walberswick. It is only now, going back through my notes, that I have rediscovered the newspaper report I must have clipped at the time describing a fatal collision on the small road that connects Dunwich with Westleton and

Walberswick. A lone walker had been knocked down and killed at a blind bend after a driver lost control of their vehicle. The car had not been found and the reporter described the incident as a hit and run. In his last message to his wife the walker had said he was lost on Dunwich Heath. Local police, the story read, wanted to talk to *another* man, a possible witness, in his mid-thirties spotted walking along the same road later that night. Only now, many years later, do I realise the story was referring to me.

Two

Falling Down

I thought it was outside disappearing
but it was disappearing in my heart
                    Frank O'Hara, 'Poem (to Franz Kline)'

I sleep alongside myself, so to speak, while I myself struggle
with dreams.

                              Franz Kafka, Diaries

. . . these fine collapses are not lies
                        Hart Crane, 'Chaplinesque'

When it seemed as if I had gone without sleep for as long as my health would allow, I agreed to visit a therapist who specialised in cases of acute anxiety. I remember little of those visits except that the attic room in which we met was light and clean and that I was invited to sit beside a casement window overlooking a public park. It was a park I knew well until, on studying the green spaces from a perch quite unfamiliar to me, I realised I had had no conception of the beautifully ordered pathways that appeared to form the outlines of a perfectly repeated W. I also remember the therapist's eyes – her name was Catherine L. – were grey and large in comparison to her other features (the details of which have long since slipped from memory), so much so that in the event of the evening closing in on us her eyes seemed to be made of their own light gazing unwaveringly into the growing darkness that surrounded us (and I was reminded of a passage in one of Andre Breton's books regarding the eyes of his allusive lover. *What was it they reflected – some obscure distress and at the same time some luminous understanding of why she was there*).

The only other thing I remember from those late afternoons, during which I'm sure I hardly spoke a word, was that Catherine was one of the few people I knew who still smoked indoors: an activity that seemed so outlawed as to be completely out-dated as if the heavily laden atmosphere of her room had leaked into the modern world from some far forgotten time. It was during one of the frequent cigarette breaks, after discussing the unrelenting pressures of my occupation at that time, that she told me of a case she had been assigned only a year or so before of an art historian afflicted by hallucinations attributed to debilitating fits of depression from which he had suffered at various times throughout his life. His name was Edward Smith, she said, he lectured in one of the old universities and had enjoyed a largely unencumbered existence until the death of his lover in a fall from a bridge. Before that moment, Smith told Catherine, who must have been sitting where I was then, his life seemed to have been lived by someone else. *It is as if when I wake up I have to begin again*, Smith said, *trying each morning to re-join who I am with whom I had been, I find myself observing the person who is acting out my life from somewhere above his head.*

After visiting Catherine regularly for a number of weeks, Edward Smith disappeared. She assumed he had broken off the treatment of his own accord, when, several months later, he returned at the usual time declaring that he had made a great discovery and as a consequence felt again like himself. He was back from New Mexico where he had been visiting the painter Agnes Martin. *I have admired her paintings all my life*, he said, *and on hearing she was ill I decided to make the journey and to speak with Martin in her place of work.* Martin was extremely welcoming and she and Smith spoke endlessly about art and pain. *Agnes told me many wonderful things*, Smith said. *She told me:* My paintings have neither objects, nor space, nor time. They are about formlessness, breaking down form. *On hearing this, I realised*, Smith said, *that my whole life had been the examination of breaking down form. As if only disintegration offered order or beauty, or any verification that I was alive. I remember pulling apart the wings of insects as a boy*, Smith said, *and in recent years*

I have felt a strong desire to return to those childhood occupations where I saw beyond doubt that things can only reveal themselves in the act of coming apart.

Catherine soon learned that none of it was true. Martin had died two decades earlier and Smith hadn't travelled anywhere. He had been at home, unable to move after discovering an obituary of Agnes Martin clipped from a newspaper many years before like a message from a stranger, Smith said, that used to be myself. *I read the obituary again and again*, Smith went on, *which included a photograph of the artist as a young woman at work in her studio with the desert beyond her door. It seemed too real to bear. And at that moment, which lasted many days, what was there for me to do*, Smith said, *but travel the great distances between the different people that make up who we are.*

By the time he was seeing Catherine, Edward Smith had been finishing a book, she told me, for which he had failed at every turn to find a publisher. The various manuscripts he had destroyed and redrafted again and again were judged by those who read them to be too fragmentary, too strange; made up as they were of long, disconnected passages drifting between one unlikely subject and the next. The book (or books), he explained to Catherine (he, it would seem had no trouble in speaking), was intended to be a meditation on the death in a freak accident of a dear and life-long friend. I later discovered that this death was not as unlikely as Smith would have Catherine believe. Smith could find no way of describing this event or to account for it openly. He instead found himself, as it were, observing his own head and shoulders bent over his writing desk, colour and sound draining away, so that the world was the equivalent of the photographs he was studying, showing any number of lost moments in time; he was left all the while to watch from the other-side of a room or street as he went about his business, reading, talking or making copious notes, all of which seemed to Smith an endless and quite pointless set of falsely related tasks. Indeed, Catherine said to me, Smith was not sure if the visions were a product of his consciousness, or whether his consciousness, those waking moments where we speak and laugh and touch one another, was a product of his own beleaguered mind.

As Catherine spoke, I felt my hands and feet go numb as if the heat was draining from my body and I could not speak. Seeing my unease, Catherine sat back and reached for a cigarette. As the smoke rose into the air between us, I wondered if it was possible for a person to judge the content of his or her hallucinations from within the suspension of reality. Then I began to think, looking down on a family picnicking in one of the patches of grass below, that such judgements might in fact be what we mean by reality and that we cannot, no matter how hard we try, divorce ourselves from these strange estimations of what might be original or new or somehow distinct from any other sequence of ordinary events. *You seem bored*, I remember Catherine saying to me, as if from a dream, when, in fact, the opposite was the case. Catherine shrugged, stubbed out her cigarette, and said it might be more beneficial for me to read the writings of Edward Smith than to sit silently in her flat on those Autumnal afternoons. *He left a great deal of it with me,* Catherine said. *For safekeeping, I suppose.* And I nodded even if we both knew nothing could be further from the truth.

During those days, I often returned to the writings of Edward Smith late at night when I was trying not to breathe for fear of disturbing those around me. I crept to a backroom and read with such appetite that, for a time, Smith's manuscript, amounting to over four hundred pages held together with dog clips and packing tape, became an extension of my insomnia. I walked about in it as if it were a set of rooms; one room led into another identical to the one previous. And yet I could do nothing but go on, moving through each copy of what had come before, as if stopping might cause something terrible to take place.

Looking back, I am grateful to Catherine for passing Smith's manuscript onto me but she could have had no idea to what extent the book would impact on my mind. While whole sections bore little relationship with one another and seemed, as far as I could tell, to float freely, like an island surrounded by mists, without any connection to what had come before or with what followed, my attention was drawn almost immediately to a recurring interest in the subject of falling, a theme that would appear again and again in a number of lengthy passages as I made my way through this bizarre forest of words. I came across Montaigne (whose name, in my mind, combined the invention of the essay with mountain climbing, falling from a horse; or Rousseau knocked off his feet by a lion-sized dog. My interest in these passages was doubled when I learned that Smith's friend and lover, S., for whom he was mourning, had driven his motorbike to Archway Bridge and thrown himself from the railings early one summer's day as the sun came up over the grey and white shadows of the city below. Reading Smith's descriptions of figures falling one after another, feverishly in pursuit (I can only assume) of his lover's ghostly outline as he fell unobserved from that bridge in North London, I came to realise I was becoming increasingly dependent on Smith's book, that it was becoming an extension of my feelings, so to speak, and that I was (as with all cowards) fleeing from what was real.

One of the strangest falls among Smith's notes, perhaps because of its connection with the fog enshrouding the early years of machine-made images, was the fall and death of William Herman Rulofson in November 1878. Rulofson was 52 years old and a very wealthy man when he slipped from a roof in San Francisco – some said he was photographing workers on the rooftop opposite – and fell fifty feet to his death. He had made his fortune in photographic portraiture, and few persons of note visiting the city were exempt from facing his camera. He captured forever the likenesses of showmen, politicians, actors and actresses, industrialists, artists, musicians, writers, critics. *Those with a public profile to peddle and could afford Rulofson's fee, as well as those who could not afford to be overlooked at a time when people everywhere sought a visual echo fit to carry their bodies across time and space, sought out the house on Sacramento Street,* writes Smith. A seasoned traveller, Rulofson showed his photographs at expositions around the globe, winning gold medals in Vienna for The Best Photograph in the World, in Chicago for the best photograph in the United States, in San Francisco for the best photograph in the city. In the year of his death, all of Paris was mesmerised by this life-size picture of his daughter, Mary Jeanette, over-painted by Carl

Schultz so that those who looked at it could not tell if it was a photo or a painting in oils. Being neither one nor the other no doubt added to its charms, as if the in-between place of the picture was where all children lived their lives, no matter how briefly.

While Rulofson was a fine photographer, Smith writes, *he was an even better host and his studio was like no other.* Spread across four floors linked by elevators powered by water, the halls were decked in exotic carpets and vast mirrors in which numerous life-size portraits mounted in guilt frames gazed back at themselves for all time. *The entire building was a spectacle,* Smith writes, with visitors making their way to its doors simply to marvel at the lifts. The decorative ironwork cages shuttled several people at once so that they disappeared into the ceiling before one's eyes  only to return empty, its cargo consumed somewhere above. Dressed in their finest the women, according to those who were there, looked like ascending angels while the men clad in the costumes of far flung lands resembled gods. *It was as if the whole place had taken on the function of a camera,* writes Smith. From the water-pumps in the basement to the liquid processing labs under the roof, those in attendance were transported along a steady stream of images, that endless river of forgetting and loss. *I have tried on many occasions,* writes Smith, *to imagine the ornate galleries and the shifting scenography of Rulofson's world where whole rooms were transformed into daguerreotype cameras.* Legend has it that Rulofson converted his darkroom into the biggest camera of all, the lens for which was mounted through a hole in the door. A glass plate was exposed as a negative and then developed in the same room to make the largest contact print of that time. The stores were filled with props and vistas wheeled out upon request. Clients could be pictured anywhere on earth: in the jungles of India amid tigers stuffed to order, alone on the folding sands of the Sahara, at sea on ocean liners braced against the spray or with their wives and children astride mules in the mountain valleys of Europe, California or Tibet. There at the centre of proceedings was the grand magician and self-made gentleman, Rulofson, who would appear as character witness for his friend and employee Eadweard Muybridge, brought to trial for murdering Henry Larkyns with a pistol; and who would decide one morning to take the air on his roof four stories above the street below. According to an obituary in the New York Times – which referred to the address on Sacramento Street close to the corner with Montgomery as his *Photograph Building* – Rulofson was killed instantly. *But of course,* writes Smith, *what is an instant?*

Smith's attention moves away (as it often did, pulling me along with it as if Smith were pursuing the half-remembered fragments of a dream dispersed between so many lighted doorways) at this point from the immediate scene on Sacramento Street to enquire after the normal weather conditions in San Francisco at the close of Autumn in any given year. *San Francisco is famous for its fog*, Smith writes. And it may well be that Rulofson, on that dank November day, straining to see through the vapours, lost his footing and fell as if through a mist. *Maybe that is why I have kept this picture of Rulofson*, writes Smith, a portrait in the romantic style in which for whatever reason his body is half-shrouded in haze. There is no false background – no dramatic staging of the self – instead Rulofson gazes out at an artificial horizon

where perhaps a loved one is returning after many weeks away or, on the brink of disappearing, the same lonely figure can be observed leaving finally never to return as all the while our onlooker dreams in solitude of the distant travel to be made by the image on his behalf. *All around him*, writes Smith, *the smokescreen of photography is rising, gently blurring the hard edge of reality that every picture, in the end, denies. Or perhaps I keep it because there is no picture of the moment Rulofson fell*, writes Smith. Rulofson struck on a pile of tin, according to the New York Times, which arrested the force of the fall and prevented mutilation of the body as if in imitation of an image fixed on a photographic plate when in reality, none was made. In another version of events Rulofson's body was found mangled on the sidewalk. *My God. I am killed* he screamed, according to witnesses, as he fell through the air perhaps in his own endeavour to arrest the moment along with all of the moments he had arrested in so many other photographs. Either way there is no evidence to show us the truth; *for all we know*, writes Smith, *Rulofson is still falling, as if in some desperate penance for his trade. And I suppose it seems only fitting after a career of fixing time that the great photographer might find himself falling forever, outside of any final account, suspended in a dreadful arc of timelessness from which there is no escape or around which no frame is drawn, in order, it would seem, to hold him in place. We are left to dream of the instant*, writes Smith, *when it eludes us completely, when time is sucked into itself and nothing remains, not even a photograph or a strip of film.*

Here, Rulofson's free fall through dream and light becomes, in Smith's writing, bizarrely anatomical. *I can't help thinking*, writes Smith, *that the missing photograph of the falling photographer is replaced, somehow, by the distance between Rulofson's eyeballs and his brain – a truly instantaneous passage housing how many immeasurable distances!* Smith's allusion to the eyes and brains of William Rulofson may, however, have more to do with Rulofson's brother, Edward.

In 1871 Edward Rulloff, as he was then known, an itinerant scholar and philologist who laboured under various aliases, was tried and hanged for murdering the clerk of a store he and his accomplices William Dexter and Al Jarvis robbed on the night of August 17th 1870. *If William H. R. was lost in a mist, Edward H. R. was a mirage*, Smith writes. Despite the lack of formal education, Edward Rulloff was versed in several tongues including German, Latin and Ancient Greek and had according to his grandest claims discovered a universal science of language. He was also, according to observers, a criminal mastermind, a dissembler and escapologist who would stop at no 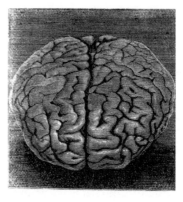 lengths to fund his intellectual endeavour. After Rulloff's hanging, Doctor George Burr secured the purchase of the deceased's head and neck for the purposes of scientific study. *I can almost hear*, writes Smith, *the serrated edge of the blade as Dr George Burr and his son Dan, sawed through the head just above the eyes, and the sucking sound, as the lid of the dead man's cranium came away revealing the flesh of the brain beneath*. The brains of murderers were of particular value for those who practised the dubious science of what was alternately known as *phrenology, craniology, craniometry* or *zoonomy*. Once Dr Burr extracted the brain and set it to one side, they removed the rest of the flesh from the skull by soaking it in acid. They found the skull to be exceptionally thick – almost half an inch of bone – and the skull to be exceptionally heavy – fifty-nine ounces, ten ounces heavier than the average for a man of Rulloff's age. The hanging, which lasted some twenty minutes, had caused intense pressure inside the skull, blood vessels were broken and the lens of Rulloff's right eye had exploded, but his features were hardly disturbed and there was no tumefaction of the face.

For the scientists, who laboured under the belief that the brain and the skull would, taken together, provide some map of a mind gone wrong, the evidence was highly suggestive. Heavy skulls were commonly associated with maniacs, heavy brains with a higher than average mental capacity. What they had here were the remains of a particularly evil type, one as much criminal as it was genius. When Dr Burr published his findings alongside pictures of Rulloff's skull and brain, the assumption was that something in their appearance, structure, or chemistry would reveal the true nature of human thought.

Failing, as a young man, in various forms of employment and, after what one report described as a series of thefts and burnings, Rulloff settled close to Enfield, in Ithaca, New York. There, his remarkable intellectual capacities catapulted him, as Smith puts it, from day labourer to the community-teaching post. He married his student Harriett Schutt, who disappeared two years later along with their six-month-old child. Neither was heard of again. On the night of their disappearance, Ruloff was seen in the early hours boarding a stagecoach, an oversized trunk among his possessions.

He was eventually tracked down to the shores of Lake Cayuga where he was working in a Saw Mill, was arrested for the abduction of Harriett, and sentenced to ten years in Auburn prison. With the assistance of the jailer's son, Al Jarvis, whom Ruloff had been schooling in German and had struck up a friendship that would last until Jarvis drowned in the Chanango river in 1870, Rulloff escaped and found his way to Meadville, Pennsylvania where he took up residence under the name of James Nelson, and was granted a teaching certificate by Reverend Dr John Barker who would later testify to Nelson's (Rulloff's) knowledge of Greek, Latin, Hebrew, French and German. In 1859 Rulloff was again arrested, this time for theft, only to be freed shortly after on a legal point for which he had established the precedent himself.

In 1860 he began ten years of a double life: the first as Edward Leurio, a teacher of languages who engaged night and day, according to various witnesses, on his etymological studies; the second as a violent thief and confidence man accompanied in both pursuits by his two young protégés Billy Dexter and the ever faithful Jarvis. Rulloff had promised his young followers that, given the time and resources to complete his manuscript, he would sell his book for $500,000 *making them rich beyond their wildest dreams*, according to Smith. Rulloff claimed to have discovered a code or system present in all words that would reveal the origins of language as both divinely ordered and modified by culture. *All words derived from four liquid sounds l, m, n, r, according to Rulloff*, writes Smith. *The sounds were attached to roots susceptible to change without loss of identity. The inarticulate coo of love, for example, connected with the l sound while the long-known sound of the "dog-letter" r related, in Rulloff's system, to the growl of hate.*

Having been convicted of murder and sentenced to death, Rulloff attempted to explain his system, in some haste, to reporters and certain leading philologists who came to visit his cell. *The whole thing depends on having such roots of words*, he told Oliver Dyer of the *New York Sun*. *Such roots are entirely unknown to modern philologists. I have*

101

discovered them, and if I had time could revolutionise the
study of language, and make it a new and living thing.

*With only the light of a kerosene lamp in his windowless
cell*, writes Smith, *Rulloff used his final letters to elaborate on
his system before it was too late.* A few examples may be given
off-hand, Rulloff writes, writes Smith, *which will point the
inquiring mind in the direction of the goal. It is a principle in
the formation of philosophical language that things, which
are opposites in meaning, are named from the same roots, in
which the elements are reversed. Take the words stir and rest
for example, the meanings of which are opposites. In stir, the
root is composed of s, t, r; in rest these are reversed – r, s, t.
Things relatively large and small are also named from the
same roots. What was most shocking to me*, writes Smith, *was
how Rulloff's language system relied on the blanking out of
certain sounds and signs – mainly vowels – in order to make
meaning connect. Rulloff could understand words only by
blowing them apart or by cancelling out and wiping away*,
writes Smith. *His work and his life collided in this way at the
very limits of language of what it was possible and not
possible to say.* In a time when men in America could invent
themselves in whatever form they might dream up, Rulloff, or
was it Leurio or Nelson, appeared to exist in these gaps, in
absent spaces, obliterations. *It can be no coincidence*, writes
Smith, *that Rulloff dispensed with the last three letters of his
family name: s, o, n. What's more* – and what makes the case
particularly sinister – *in the same way that words disappeared
in the world of Edward Rulloff, so did bodies.* In his prison
cell in the days before his hanging, taking a break one
presumes from writing his final words, Rulloff told his friend

and publisher, Ham Freeman, he had disposed of Harriett Schutt's body in the waters of Lake Cayuga. Rulloff declined to address the fate of his daughter. *Most were convinced*, Smith writes, *Rulloff murdered them both.*

Like his brother, photography plays a role in the story and this might be why I see Rulloff in my dreams, writes Smith. At dawn on Friday 19th August 1870 a passer-by spotted a corpse floating facedown among the boulders close to the Chanango River Bridge. At almost the same moment another body was discovered further down stream snagged in tree-roots close to the riverbank. The bodies were eventually dragged ashore to the cheers of a growing crowd. Two days before, George Merrick had been shot in the head protecting his riverside store from burglars. The two strangers lying dead on the banks of the wide Chenango, their bodies swollen and faces blackening in the sun were, the people of Binghampton knew, responsible. The bodies were moved to the undertakers but the summer heat and the saturation of the flesh hastened decomposition and Seneca Bullock a local photographer was called.

Since he needed more light, Smith writes, *Bullock had some men lay the bodies on planks and prop them against a barn outside.* The picture he made was used to identify the men as William Dexter and Charles Curtis, also known as, Al

Jarvis. *Set in that way*, writes Smith, *it strikes me that nothing was immune to the new arrangements of machine-made images, not even the dead.*

Late at night, studying the picture of Dexter and Jarvis, which Smith had clipped from somewhere and pasted into his text, I suddenly realised that my room had turned a milky blue. I looked up for the first time, it seemed, in hours at the television continuing its silent report on a diving contest somewhere on the other side of the world. I watched in a trance as the synchronised pairs performed their twisting descent through the air in exact likeness of one another and I saw their strange resemblance to the two men in Bullock's picture. *Or was it one man*, Smith writes, *doubled as he passed into the watery mirror world of the dead?* I must have finally fallen asleep, as I saw each body falling alongside its mirror image, like stones sinking to the bottom of a lake.

x x
x x
x x
x x
x x
x x
x x

When William Rulofson was discovered on the sidewalk of Sacramento Street in San Francisco in 1878 a miniature picture of an unknown man was found in his coat. Nobody knew who it was. *But it was not that the man in the picture was unknown, writes Smith*, but that William H. Rulofson, the most famous portrait photographer in California, *had spent his whole life hiding any connection between himself and the head of the dead man in the frame.* The picture was of his brother, Edward, the now famous murderer and philologist recently hanged at Tomkins County Jail. *As the funeral procession snaked its way through downtown and the city's photographic studios closed for the day, few stopped to wonder if Rulofson had been threatened or bribed, or if the photograph in his pocket was a particular form of suicide note. It should come as no surprise,* writes Smith, *that Rulofson's studio, with all of its grandeur, would be destroyed by the fires that consumed San Francisco for days on end in the wake of an enormous earthquake in 1906 that lasted less than a minute.*

~

Some months later, my note-taking was interrupted when I received a phone call from Catherine L. She asked how I was and apologised that the therapy sessions had not been more beneficial. As she spoke, I could see again her eyes brighter than everything in the room and for a split second the outlines of her face flashed up in front of me like a frame left in accidentally at the end of a film. When my eyes returned to the untended objects of my room, including the dust strewn floor littered with used tickets for buses I could not recall boarding, I told her I didn't think the therapy sessions were the problem. There was a pause before she told me the reason for her call. *I thought you should know that Edward Smith was found dead yesterday.* She said, *by all accounts it was sudden.* For a moment I didn't know what she was talking about. Then I remembered the strange bundle of papers she had given me the previous autumn. By now it was late July and the sun shone fiercely even though the day had barely begun. I opened a window. Not a breath of air entered the room. I asked Catherine if she wanted Smith's manuscript back. *What manuscript?* She said. *Oh, I see what you mean. I shouldn't think so. Anyway*, she went on, *I thought you should know.*

I thanked her for calling and the phone went dead. Not knowing what else to do, I pushed my notes to one side and opened Smith's manuscript to a page entitled: On the Subject of Mirrors and Eternity. It began by describing a walk Smith had made when he was a boy, in the company of an aunt who took him as part of what she called his wider education to the hills of southern Germany where he was to come upon the most beautiful lake he had ever seen. For several paragraphs he attempts to account for the impression this view had on him as a young man. His argument, if that's what it was, suggests the reflective qualities of the water on that particular day, where not a wisp of wind disturbed the surface of the lake which stretched before him like a mirror as far as the eye could see, were responsible for fixing the scene in his memory. For a long time he gazed at the perfect likeness of the opposite shore – a bank of ancient sycamore trees, and beyond them dark pines above which the snow capped mountains of the valley towered over everything. He wanted to leave this world, he writes, and join the upside down version in the lake which seemed somehow more perfect, more blessed with possibility, than the real world in which he stood.

What follows is a long passage on the play of optics and

memory that defines both what we see and how we see it before the scientific speculation breaks off again and Smith recounts his return to the same lake as a grown man where a three-day storm confined the visitors to their chambers. Even if Smith had dared to venture beyond the confines of the alpine resort he would have seen very little of the scenery, so closed in was the rain and the mist. On the morning he was due to depart, utterly frustrated by the fruitlessness of his visit, he read in a newspaper of a man who had drowned in the lake a few weeks earlier. According to the report this father of three, who was well liked by everyone who lived in the vicinity did not return to his belongings left by a small jetty from which he swam every morning, as he had done since he was a boy. Divers searched the lake but no body had been recovered. *It was as if*, Smith writes, *the man had fallen out of the world.* Yet the details of the undoubtedly tragic story were not what captivated Edward Smith so much as the photograph in the paper of the spot where the man lost his life. The photograph was an exact replica of the view Smith had seen as a boy.

Smith could not breathe. He felt he was drowning in the same air sufficient for those around him to continue living their lives: lives that held together and did not fall apart. For many years, Smith did not return to that part of the world. Ever since that

time, he could not be sure if what he remembered was the actual lake or the picture he had discovered in the newspaper on the eve of his second storm-hit journey. His fragmentary recollections, as far as I could tell, were meant to serve as notes toward a longer chapter on verisimilitude in art and nature. But this was one of many sections of the manuscript which to this day remain unresolved. Nonetheless, it was clear to me, in my stricken state at that time, what Smith was attempting to outline (although I'm not sure the same is true today) and I wondered if it was odd that I could feel closer to a person once they were gone, once I knew there was no possibility of ever meeting them face to face.

Catherine's phone call came at a bad time. For weeks I worked in my room alone, making notes almost automatically from the moment I got up until I tried late in the evening to sleep. On nights when it was too much I put on my shoes and travelled through outer parts of London's northern most boroughs, Barnet, Enfield, the wooded roadways of Waltham Forest, following paths close to the outermost edge of that vast metropolis which seemed so all-encompassing as to have no marked boundary at all.

One night Anne ran after me into the street. *Where are you going?* she said. *Why do you keep going away?*

I knew whatever I did would not be enough. When I was gone, often for the night, I spoke to no one. One morning, not long after I had heard the news of Edward Smith, I came home to discover my key no longer worked in the lock. Two small bags had been left behind a wall. One containing three sets of clothes and a spare pair of shoes the other the contents of my desk along with a bundle of unopened post and an envelope with my name on it. Nausea swept through me and it was then that the second memory from the hospital – Anne's scream from another room where she had been told the baby in her womb had died – broke the silence of my mind. I did the wrong thing. I picked up the bags and walked away.

I took a room close to the Barnet Road, narrow and rundown in those parts, but which, I was led to believe, wound its way north, like a river beyond the boundaries of London as far as Cambridge, having formed the Great North Road to Edinburgh along a coaching route dating back to the time of Medieval pilgrims. When I wasn't working, I sat in a café run by a Cypriot family. In the evening, they served wine and spirits. I took the same table, in a corner, from where I could study a photograph hanging on the wall between baskets of plastic ivy. The photograph showed the bluest river I had ever seen. A white suspension bridge spanned the breadth of water and it was clear the photographer, whoever he of she might have been, considered the bridge to be a significant feat of engineering. Whenever I looked at the picture of the bridge I was struck by how incongruous it appeared and wondered what it was I was studying: the picture or the strange set of circumstances, largely invisible, that had brought the picture to that place.

One evening, on looking up from my notes, close to tears and tracing almost automatically the lace-like lines of the spectral bridge, I became aware of the restaurant owner standing at my side. Ever since I had first entered the restaurant I could not let go of the idea that she had taken a strong disliking toward me. Pretending not to notice, I looked back at the table. I realised I had been reading the same page of Smith's manuscript again and again. This was, no doubt, the kind of behaviour that made Eleanor (I later learned this was her name) despair of certain men. Before she returned to the front of the restaurant I was sure I saw her shake her head, and it was some time before I could recover the strength necessary to read on.

~

On the 24th September 1950, writes Smith, *Humphrey Jennings picked his way over boulders toward the blue Mediterranean.* Stumbling on broken ground high above the sea he caught glimpse of a rock lizard disappearing between grey and white stones. The flash of colour affected Jennings deeply, filling his body with loathing, like a man who realises he is on the wrong track. Humphrey Jennings looked up at the sky. In his diaries, the filmmaker complained continuously of tinnitus: the incessant sound of bells, he wrote, far in the distance but closer than anything happening nearby. He shook his head. On the beach below a fire had been started. Jennings watched as men threw knots of worn out rope and broken boat wood onto the flames as a column of smoke rose into the empty sky. One of the men looked up at Jennings and put his hand in the air. Jennings did not return his signal. He turned and carried on over the rocks.

Some way behind, the ever faithful Dillon Barry was following. The path was getting steeper. From where she was, Jennings looked like a drawing, his legs and arms were pencil marks rubbed away and re-drawn every time he moved. Or an insect observed under a microscope. Barry was sure she had been here before but she did not know when or how, perhaps before she was born or perhaps she had already died. *We are memories of the dead*, she would later write. *Cut loose and homeless with no one to chain them to their lives.* That was the first time she slipped. When she looked up Jennings was ahead of her a cardinal point in that land of grey and white and blue. The second time she slipped, Jennings was gone.

Barry and Jennings had travelled that morning from their hotel in Athens to the Island of Poros, scouting locations for The Changing Faces of Europe, one of seven documentaries paid for by the Marshall Plan. Jennings, ironically, had chosen to focus on health. In the weeks leading up to their trip, he had travelled extensively through northern and southern Europe shooting footage and drafting scripts. When they reached Greece they were forced to stop. Word had come through that the production company wanted the film to be made using the new Technicolor technology. But his team had only ever worked in black and white and the colour equipment was heavy and cumbersome. It was very different less than a decade earlier when Jennings and his team had occupied, like an invading army, several square miles of London's East End. *We have more or less taken over Stepney and Wapping, roped off streets, organised locals and so on*, Jennings wrote in a letter to his wife. The plan was to restage the Blitz from only three summers before: a black and white nightmare that is, for those watching, both beautiful and unbearable. In Only Connect, his essay on Humphrey Jennings, Lindsay Anderson describes Jennings' fire film: *As night falls an alarm begins to wail; a fire unit is called out to action at a riverside warehouse, where fire threatens an ammunition ship drawn up at the wharf; the fire is mastered; a man is lost; the ship sails with the morning tide. Thus*, writes Smith rather grandly, copying Anderson's words into his own work with the same magpie impulse with which Humphrey Jennings assembled his collage-like masterpiece, Pandemonium, *the filmmaker-poet is able to build a story from partial images flashing across the mind like streaks of chalk across a blackboard.* At any moment the night might be cut in two by the darker form of ladders extended into the sky or faces might flash into resolution lit by invisible flames as firemen direct water cannons resembling film projectors – *beams of whiteness cutting lines through the ever-present black*, as Smith puts it – into the hottest part of the blaze. Capturing the flare of an incendiary in a black London street at the moment it both annihilated the world and made it unbearably visible is what Jennings called Flash Time: this was his art, one of lines and shapes drawn in the air, outlines that are fragile, passing, incomplete, and Jennings was suddenly being made to choose between it and the new colour technologies, *the way certain writers are made to choose between poetry and prose*, as Smith puts it. He knew in his heart it could not be done.

By the end of 1943 Jennings was exhausted, according to Smith, from re-performing in black and white pictures the best likeness of what the firemen and women acting in his Blitz film were, no doubt, trying to forget. *Reading nothing*, Jennings wrote at the time. *Life concerned with a burning roof – smoke fire water – men's faces and thoughts: a tangle of hose, orders shouted in the dark – falling walls, brilliant moonlight – dust, mud, tiredness until nobody is quite sure where the film ends and the conditions of making begin. A real fire,* he writes, *could not be more tiring and certainly less trouble* and it seemed that for Jennings, in order to make a world, the world had to first be destroyed. *And yet, for whatever reason,* writes Smith, *it was not simply with fire and burning that Jennings was preoccupied, like someone made ill by pyromania, but with a landscape lost in smoke. Some of the most striking scenes in* Fires Were Started *are those depicting the early hours of the following day,* writes Smith: *the dust settling in morning light, steam, smouldering timbers, the glare of the sun on the soaking wet streets. The ruined city,* writes Smith, *is shot in fragments through a haze.* Of course, for Jennings, smoke connected with power and destruction; *his unfinished book filled to bursting with skies blackened by the billowing fumes of factories, power stations, coalmines and trains,* writes Smith, *suggests that smoke is not a by-product of what is happening – smoke is what is happening. In fact, you could say,* Smith writes, *history was personalised, for Jennings, in smoke. My favourite picture of him shows Jennings sitting in a carefully lighted room. The background is geometric and dark while the pipe-smoke he has at that moment exhausted – the contents of his lungs, or is*

it his soul, Smith wonders – *hangs with supernatural luminosity in the air before his eyes. What, I wonder, does Jennings see?* asks Smith, *for I'm sure if one were to look it would be possible to find a whole tradition of portrait photography in which the artist or writer, in the grip of metaphysical meditation, is smoking. There is, for instance, that well known picture of Albert Camus, a car-crash victim and now a ghost, smoking in a bar, or Picasso blowing smoke onto a glass, or this one of Frank Stella, forging a smoke ring made plastic by the exposure so that, taken together, each lone exhalation looks like a word or letter from a peculiar alphabet forming stories you cannot read – like smoke signals rising over a hill – which tell you, nonetheless, that somewhere something is horribly wrong. It is in the end the language of the dead,* writes Smith, *to speak in zeroes – where something and nothing alternate so freely that it is entirely possible, suddenly, to lose track of the difference between sensations and the words we use to pin them down.*

Did you know, writes Smith, as if he were talking to me directly, *that the current of a nerve impulse is a sort of electrochemical smoke ring about two inches long travelling along the nerve at a speed of as much as 300 feet per second! This may be why in 1927,* Smith writes, *amid the smoke of Ernst Jöel and Fritz Fränkel's hashish experiments conducted for*

114

purely scientific purposes, you realise, Walter Benjamin found himself unable to decide if he wished to be with company or alone as those around him submerged into the décor of the room. Terrified by what he called a bad simultaneity, the German scholar, as soon as he was able, reached for his shoes and left only to find, as he took a table overlooking the Marseille docks, he was unable to order a meal. Instead, he felt for a pen inside his coat and wrote these words: I learned as a child to disguise myself in words, which really were clouds. *I am sure I can see in this picture of Humphrey Jennings*, writes Edward Smith, *smoking his pipe in the image of a shaman or Sherlock Holmes, the same loneliness in the company of other people – people he cared for deeply – and I often think that that time in my life, trapped somewhere between then and now, is shrouded in the same mists I've seen in his films, those grey vapours holding light in the air and out of which the tired figures (played not by actors but by serving firemen and the residents of Stepney, Wapping and Bow, all of whom are by now most certainly dead) appeared and then were gone. Rather than recording events from the lives of those I haven't met, those others have in fact invented the stories that, as far as I can tell*, writes Smith, *make up who I am.*

While in Athens on the day before his fatal trip to Poros, Jennings was photographed riding on donkeys in the streets, laughing and singing with locals. The air was warm and Jennings was among free people far from the shores of England and Walberswick where he imagined, as a lonely youth, other worlds beyond the white sand dunes which

barrier the marsh from the black North Sea. *I personally haven't found any of these photographs,* Smith writes, *but I do have a picture of Jennings standing in the doorway of his home in Camden Town at the end of the Second* World *War. He is smiling and confident. England is a different place. The war has changed things, he hopes, for good. Looking back on that time, it strikes me,* writes Smith, *that Jennings is standing at a threshold between one world and the next like a figure on a bridge. On one side of this strange divide there is the new era of saturated pictures appearing more like the world than the world itself, while on the other is the older abstract art of contrasts observed as closely as possible, fading into the distance. In fact, when Jennings met Andre Breton in London in the summer of 1936, surely,* writes Smith, *Breton would have greeted the younger man with the same lines from Murnau's* Nosferatu, *with which he greeted all new friends: Passé le pont les fantômes vinrent à sa rencontre' – On the other side of the bridge, the phantoms come to meet him. And yet, looking at the photo of him with Breton, I often think it is as if Jennings is standing at the other side of that bridge, where he has come to meet us and tell us, he is not the ghost.*

I have one last picture of Jennings, Smith writes, *in which he is standing in front of a great fog rising from what looks like a doorway into the earth. I have studied it for so many* years that I have long since forgotten where the picture is from. On one evening, while running a bath, I opened a window and the picture fell out of a book. I stood up and found myself wandering after Jennings who, as if he could bear things no longer, had abandoned his station finally and walked away from me into the mist. At first I walked with the same half-finished hands of all my family, writes Smith, outstretched in front of me until I was surprised to find the going unobstructed and I pursued the figure with some ease through the thickening gloom.

After sometime however, as I realised he was on the verge of disappearing, I tried to call out. I must have made some sound because he turned and smiled. I waved as if from across the street to an old friend or relative but he did not wave back. I wanted to ask if the people in his films were always somehow gone, or if they had to have been there all along otherwise we could not exist? But I could not speak and I felt myself choking in the fog. As I looked into his eyes, I realised, as if in the instant when the aperture closes and the shutter comes down, he was looking at someone else. I must have

passed out, writes Smith. The bath had overflowed. I stood up, shut off the tap and observed my own handprints on the wet tiled floor. They looked like prints made by a child. Like black and white negatives captured many years in the past.

117

We can never be sure, writes Smith, *to what extent our observations are of our own making. Jennings combined what others had seen with the pictures he carried in his heart because he knew in the end they could not be owned by him. Perhaps he was dogged by the same idea as he walked out onto the Poros cliff seeking a particular view of the Athenian shore across the water, one based on books or pictures he had seen while growing up in Walberswick on the Suffolk coast. But he never found what it was he was looking for. Instead he disappeared for a moment, left the world of images, and was gone.*

Reading Edward Smith's work on Humphrey Jennings, that great chronicler of ghosts, while waiting for my drink in Eleanor's café, I thought of everything I couldn't keep hold of or make contact with or connect. I realised then that I had left more of myself behind than I could bear to take away—

The closest record of the moment Jennings fell, writes Smith in a side note, *is a memo written by Dillon Barry after she had retrieved his body from the foot of the cliffs. He was lying on his side with his head against a rock, halfway in the water*, she writes. *I climbed down and lifted him out of the sea. He was unconscious and breathing with difficulty and covered with blood, which seemed to come mainly from a cut on his hand. I raised his head and put a tourniquet on his wrist and went back over the rocks round the corner of the bay and called a boat*. Jennings died that evening in a military hospital in Poros from a brain haemorrhage. Barry accompanied his body back to Athens on a Greek Naval vessel at three o'clock in the morning. Looking out at the dark waters it would not have been lost on Barry the irony of

Jennings' death. *Here was a man*, Smith writes, *who had survived the obliterations of war, risked his own life to shoot* Fires Were Started, *survived the flying glass and the falling masonry of the Blitz and had gone ashore under heavy fire with the marines during the invasion of Sicily and returned cheerful and unscathed, only to be killed on a tranquil Greek island while working on a film about the promises of peace.*

Before boarding the boat the police took a statement from Barry. *But as the questions were asked by the naval commander who spoke very little English and were taken down by a police officer who spoke no English at all with the help of an Admiral who came in later and spoke only French, I cannot really remember what the questions asked*, Barry writes in her memo. *For whatever reason, this breakdown in communication, this failure to connect affected me most deeply when I read Barry's record of events*, writes Smith. *She could not meet anybody in her grief. Instead she escorted the dead body in silence across the narrow sea at its blackest, in the hours before dawn, from one dark shore to the other.*

It must have been after eleven when Eleanor had completed her final rounds, and I imagined I could hear hooves on the empty street outside. I waited for the carriage or what I assumed would be a horse-drawn hearse, the kind it is still possible to see in London suburbs on weekday afternoons as if journeying out of some macabre longing for a time before motorisation, but neither materialised in the misted glass that barriered those exiled in Eleanor's dining-room from the world outside. Trying to avoid Eleanor's eyes as she dried glasses behind the bar, I looked around and, on expecting to find myself alone, was quite startled by a man and his daughter sitting at a corner table almost as darkened as my own. The man, who looked to be my age, sat with his back to me, his attention fixed on the door; perhaps in expectation of a guest or it might have been the case that I was not the only late night patron to have heard the sound of hooves. The girl, no more than five or six years old, was sitting with her head in her hand, bent over a book, and I was reminded suddenly of a painting I had once seen by Matisse, who had painted his daughter bent over a book as if she was the inhabitant of a distant land he would forever be unable to reach. By the time this image had returned to me from the back of my mind, so to speak, the girl at the table had made the apparently short journey across the room and sat down next to me. *What are you reading?* she said. I thought about trying to explain and I looked over to where her father was sitting alone. *I am reading Peter Pan,* she said. *It is about children who fly away – far away, past the stars and over the sea – to a magic island where they will never grow up. Have you read it?* I nodded.

Julia, the man called from his table, *leave him alone.* He stood up and walked over. *You're disturbing him,* he said. *Get your things. It's late.*

She went to collect her coat, which had fallen to the floor behind her chair and her book. *Work?* the man said, looking at the pages spread out in front of me. *She thinks I am a painter,* he said. *That's what she tells her friends: that her father is very good at painting.* He laughed and then he whispered: *I have never painted anything in my life.* I looked at him. I wanted to tell him that everything would be fine and that he was in possession of more than he realised. But my eyes fell on the chair where Julia had been sitting and I could not bring myself to speak. When I looked up, he was speaking to Eleanor at the bar. They kissed and Eleanor hugged the child before the pair went out into the street. When Eleanor brought me the bill, I told her that my daughter loved to read. She stared at me. What daughter? She said. You should bring her here. I looked at the chair again. I can't, I said. For a moment the café went dark and, the following day, as I watched the sun creep over the rooftops, I realised I had no recollection of how, at some point during the previous evening, I had found my way back to my room.

~

On evenings when the café closed and I did not wish to return to my room I walked without aim along the empty streets, pausing at the doorways of late-night bars before carrying on. On one of these journeys through the night, where I often found myself wondering if I was in fact following some silent transit of the dead, I stopped in my tracks at the sight of a shop window, one I must have passed in daylight hours a hundred times without noticing the barren display of wall lamps and plastic chandeliers which had collected so much dust it appeared the entire enterprise had been abandoned along with so many of the beleaguered shop-fronts and rundown houses on Barnet Road. But on this occasion some unseen hand had illuminated the window so that each fitting, glowing with its own spectral incandescence, combined with the others to create a blinding white square at the centre of that otherwise desolate street.

121

I don't know how many times I went out of my way to pass the shop again but not once in the weeks and months afterwards did I find the window illuminated. When I returned in order to take this picture, the shop name (which struck me as quite incongruous given the circumstances and which I can only assume was intended to expressed a playful if misplaced sense of Parisian glamour) put me in mind of a passage I would later read in Smith's book devoted to the illustrious lives of Auguste and Louis Lumiere and the films they made at a time when the streets of London had made their interminable advance this far into the fields of Middlesex. *Of all their films*, Smith writes, *I am to this day most haunted by a particularly granular street scene captured on what must have been a perfectly sun-filled morning in late July 1897 showing, of all things, a wall falling down. I often see the demolition in my dreams*, Smith writes. *I see the workers hack away with pickaxes while another man winds away at a jack. The wall, which must be a foot thick and two yards high, sends a cloud of dust into the air as it crashes down, revealing beyond where it stood the remains of an abandoned home. Louis, in great agitation, pacing up and down arms waving, overseeing the operation like the conductor of some grand symphony, runs through his apparently improvised routine until it becomes apparent that the world has without warning, turned back on itself. The pickaxes swing in reverse pulling at what they had taken apart, the dust evaporates, the wall flies up and, the scene, restored proves as much as anything that all of our works are haplessly absurd and of no real consequence. I cannot hide my astonishment*, Smith writes. *It is the origin of all romantic*

123

stories to bring down the world and set it right again as if nothing ever happened. But that is the problem exactly, writes Smith. *Nothing would be as it was.*

~

Some time later I learned the circumstances of Edward Smith's death. He had been staying on the shore of Lake Geneva, in the shadows of the Swiss Alps, suffering more than ever with depression and hallucinations. On his last night in a hotel in Montreux he told a bartender he had learned to communicate with goats native to that part of the Alps and hoped to follow them high into the hills where they would share their ancient secrets with him.

One dawn, he set off walking in a new pair of boots. The maître d' observed him from the terrace where he had served Smith coffee. *He disappeared over the rise*, he said. He was the last person to see Edward Smith alive. Locals who knew the route told whoever wanted to know that he must have fallen through a crack in the glacier. On sunny days it is quite common to be blinded by the snow and lose sight of the track. There are sheer drops on either side of the pathways in that area many of which are over a thousand feet in height. Smith's body was found the following winter, frozen solid, and I wondered if anyone had thought to let him thaw, to see if he might come back to life.

Smith had lost his way before. Among the final notes he made before he disappeared Smith describes walking the lower tracks close to the hotel as they rise toward more exposed passes between the steep cliffs. He had read about missile installations made during the Cold War in bunkers dug beneath the mountains close to Montreux and stood for a long time in the freezing cold waiting for the tremors to rise up from the ground, signs as it were of a subterranean existence defined by absolute invisibility the sole aim of which was the obliteration of civilisations many hundreds of miles from that white wilderness. *Closer than you think*, Smith writes. While waiting, poised like some forgotten piece of machinery, a snowstorm blew up all-but blinding Edward Smith. The features of the landscape disappeared and Smith was convinced, suddenly, that he was floating through space, adrift within a force he could not control. *I might as well have been in outer space*, he writes. *In zero gravity neither floating away nor falling towards but a body severed of its relations, one that never connects.* Perhaps Smith had in mind a radio programme he had heard whilst listening to the World Service in his room a few days earlier, his bloodshot eyes following the hairline cracks – like rivers seen from the moon – lining the faded plasterwork of his ceiling. A specialist in astronautics who worked in a Florida university described what the interviewer had tried to call space walking. *Space walking is not walking* she said. *It has nothing to do with the ways we move about the surface of the earth lifting dust or dirt or pushing down grasses. When you leave the earth's atmosphere and enter outer space you are in free fall. You cannot prepare your self for this*, she said. *You leave no footprints; you leave no trace.* There is nothing in our lives on earth that resembles free fall in space.

Aleksi Leonov, described as the first man to walk in space on the 18 March 1965, writes Smith, said something similar: *Before me – blackness: an inky black sky studded with stars*

that glowed but did not twinkle; they seemed immobilised. Nor did the sun look the same as when seen from earth. It had no aureole or corona; it resembled a large incandescent disc embedded in the velvet black of the sky of outer space. Space itself appeared as a bottomless pit. It will never be possible to see the cosmos the same way on earth. It is hard to know what to make of Smith's account of the snowstorm and these travels in space. The passage cuts off abruptly without saying what happened to him in that field of white. Instead, Smith pasted a picture of Michael Snow, the filmmaker and musician, walking in the white mountains of French Canada. *When I first saw this picture,* writes Smith, *I could not take my eyes off Snow's left foot. It is a blur, as if he is stepping into or out of disappearance, a reminder – as if one were needed – that in every step we make there is the possibility of falling...* And with that Smith's prose, as usual, changes tack.

When Michael Snow was a boy in Ontario his father was blinded by a dynamite blast, Smith writes. *He worked in the silver mines close to where Snow grew up. His eyeballs, already dilated in the darkness, had no defence against the flare. I think that's why Michael Snow made films,* Smith writes. *After reading about Michael Snow's father, blindness changed in my imagination from a fearful darkness to a white space like a side of writing paper or an empty museum. Of course it was not just the*  fact of what happened, but the name attached to its account – Snow – like the title of a book or a story – that did this to me, writes Smith. *Whenever it snows up here, it looks like the television has broken down; it looks like an archaeology of falling,* Smith writes from his Alpine hotel room, *if you can imagine such a thing? I now realise, I have been trying to do so ever since.*

Tucked into this section of Smith's text, I found an article torn from a Canadian arts magazine about a telephone conversation between Cecil Taylor, Ad Reinhardt, Aldo Tambelini, _____, _____, _____, and Michael Snow in August 1967. Seven men on shared telephone lines connecting Toronto and New York, there to talk about the colour black. For Reinhradt black was aesthetic. For Taylor and Tambolini, black was social. Michael Snow said nothing, except that his father went blind at the end of his life. As the conversation becomes increasingly heated, Snow's silence seems to gather

itself into a strange and elusive space within the phone record. *The only time I ever heard real silence*, writes Edward Smith, in a note on the article, *was on the telephone. Not the phones people carry everywhere but the ones plugged into walls in rooms, on bedside tables, in kitchens, on desks. Hemmed in by the hard reality of a particular room in a particular place, a silence between two people on the telephone feels like death*, writes Smith, *like the effect of heavy snowfall on the ground. I may be connected with another human being on the opposite side of the world and yet more often than not I find myself staring into a patch of dark and light like the space at the back of the eye, or the space behind pictures; the space, as it were, behind what I can see. That is why I stay away from phones*, writes Smith.

Looking closely at Michael Snow listening in on his line to Toronto, saying nothing – as if waiting for a signal, not in a room in New York City, but in a radio station high up in a central region of an unpopulated mountain range – I was overcome by the uneasy sensation that my wires were crossing with those of Edward Smith. I decided then, at that moment

in the café, to call Anne. We hadn't spoken for several weeks and I felt a sudden urge to hear her voice. A man answered and told me that Anne did not want to speak to me. I could hear children's voices and music in the background. I wanted to scream at this man and push my hand into his face but I didn't say anything.

Listen, he said. *Try again tomorrow.*

What tomorrow? I wondered. What form would it take? I had been told on numerous occasions the only cure for grief is time. But as I listened to the lost sounds of my home in the shadows of the telephone connection I felt the surge of an ongoing moment, the terrible vertigo of a now with no future or past only a before and an after that were inaccessible, gone, the way the world of hard facts and irrefutable evidence must appear to a person falling through the air. The phone went dead and I looked up at that fearsome white bridge.

As if to dramatise Smith's association of telephones with death, Ad Reinhardt, the other participant in that historical afternoon in New York City, died suddenly in his Mid Town studio just as the article in the Canadian magazine went to press. *Reinhardt's transcript must have seemed like a voice from the grave, like a ghost on the line*, Smith writes. Shocked and upset, the editors dedicated the issue to Reinhardt's memory. After about 1962, Ad Reinhardt painted nothing but a black square as high as a person and as wide as a person's outstretched arms, again and again, in a terminal attempt to paint the world's final painting. Reinhardt painted these black squares in precisely the same way, stooped over a canvas laid flat to the floor as if he were painting an opening in the earth. In the year before he died, the Jewish Museum in New York exhibited some 120 of the paintings, all untitled except for a number. Judging by the only installation shot I have from the time, the exhibition of so many black squares looks like a redaction of painting, as if the history of applying paint to canvas had been blacked out, exchanged with a series of anonymous place holders for what had gone before and for what, if anything, would come after.

Looking through a library copy of Lucy Lippard's book on Ad Reinhardt published the following year, Smith writes, *I can't help but notice that the quite startling colour plates, reproductions that I imagine have very little to do with the original paintings, have, over time and use, marked the facing page with a reverse impression – a series of ghostly tracings, like tracks left by tyres on a road. Indeed, the actual paintings were often damaged, either in acts of vandalism or in attempts to see the paintings as closely as possible. The picture leaves the studio as a purist, abstract, non-objective work of art,* Reinhardt said according to Smith, *and returns as a record of everyday (surrealist, expressionist) experience ('chance' spots,*

defacements, hand-markings, accidents, 'happenings', scratches) and is repainted, restored into a new painting painted in the same old way, again and again, over and over, until it is just 'right' once more. There could be no end, it turns out, writes Smith, *except in endlessness – whether that be endless repetition or endless reproduction or in being endlessly restored.*

Here Smith breaks off to reflect on Reinhardt's infamous slideshows, where for some five hours he would present over two thousand photographs taken from his travels in Europe and the Middle East as well as from books and magazines. The slides showed buildings, objects, things made by people that had some significance for the history of art. *For reasons I cannot completely explain,* writes Smith, *Reinhardt's photographic tour of the world has always haunted the way I think about artworks as sites of terrible destruction and loss.* Those who saw the slideshow likened it to a film of extraordinary concentration as each of the slides were shown one after the other for a maximum of five seconds each, too fast for the images to be studied, too slow to bombard the mind. Yet here was the world. One made of pictures as loosely connected to one another as they were disconnected from the things they were intended to depict. A journey through what is and isn't there. *It must have been a case of leaving yourself at the door,* Smith writes, *of dissolving into the sequence of images whose only meaning was the sequence itself. But what was it that happened between each slide, in the black transitions, as the machine replaced one picture with the next? I realised suddenly that the black paintings were like these gaps in the space and time between pictures.*

The continuous replacement, reproduction and cancellation was not an act of forgetting, but its performance. What it showed was that nothing could hold in place or be remembered as it was, but could only drift in and out of register, never taking you as it goes, only leaving you behind. And when all I could do was to stare into the emptiness of those terrible days after S. fell from Archway Bridge, it seemed that Reinhardt's black square was an image I had made myself, writes Smith, *one I had since put away, in the event of putting myself away, only to resurface when I least expected it, like a feeling from a time when I could remember how I felt. Like falling through space. This is of course the most unreliable part of remembering.* While most people think that it is a failure of memory to lose sight of some part of our past, it seems to me that memory is not about preservation, of holding things in place. *On the contrary,* writes Smith, *memory is an agent of destruction. It goes out of its way to obliterate and erase.*

~

I was, in the end, prescribed drugs to help me sleep. The drugs provided temporary relief but it soon became clear that a side effect of the medication was vivid and often violent dreams. I never had the chance to meet with Edward Smith except in the depths of these black and medicated comas. In one dream, I travelled to Lucerne in order to see for myself the icy blue peaks that so hypnotised Smith. From the window of the lakeside hotel it was possible to discern the separation of the outward atmosphere into ethereal blades defining, in that moment, an infinite variety of pale whites, greys and pinks.

Hooping wildly, gulls cut through the air and I began to wonder what I had been thinking.

There was a knock and for the first time I noticed the details that made up my room: the small, freshly-made bed, the sink, the cracked floor tiles and, beneath my feet, the worn green rug. The feeling of having left something behind, a vital document or record, was overwhelming and the dream shifted to another time when, in the act of performing, upon request – always at the whim and service of others – a handstand the way I often did as a boy, the contents of my pockets, everything I had been holding onto unthinkingly and which I had up until then forgotten completely, fell to the floor and rolled away.

I opened the door. The man from the hotel desk handed me a large gimlet and for a moment I was aware of nothing but the transparent cubes of ice hanging beneath the surface, replaying, while they could, some private form of music. As I looked at the glass, I saw the city inverted in the lake and it seemed to me that only shadows and the movements of the air mark our presence in such a place. We are gone before we arrive.

The scene changed once more and, again empty handed, I made for an ice-cream stand where a tall young man passed me a cornet, taking my money as he spoke in animated German with a woman who was equally tall and equally youthful; neither of them looked at me. Walking as best I could in the fashion of somebody completely at ease with their surroundings (which was of course the original purpose of these resort towns which at the end of the Nineteenth Century sprung up along lakeshores, and where any personal venture could do nothing but turn out as planned) it dawned on me that the young couple were discussing Edward Smith.

When I found him, he was standing on a terrace in such proximity to the shore that he appeared to be floating on the water. For some reason, in each of these dreams Smith is wearing a hat; I have no idea if this was something he was accustomed to doing. But there he was leaning against a bar, or sitting behind a desk, or looking out to sea with the air of someone measuring distances outside of ordinary physical space, in a boater, or a beret, or a high red fez. On seeing me he would lift his headgear and tilt his head to one side before offering me his seat. All of these bizarre, even outmoded, gestures appeared completely natural as I sat within touching distance and waited for him to speak. He would begin to pace, arms clasped behind his back. The subject was always otherworldly but it was possible to trace some association with the room or the landscape that framed our meeting. *Have you ever ascended the staircases of Carlo Scarpa*, Smith told me. I assumed he was drunk.

No, I said.

Scarpa's staircases in Verona are beautiful, Smith said, *but dangerous. If you approach them in the wrong way you are bound to fall. Scarpa himself died after falling down a flight of stairs in Japan in 1978. But perhaps being prone to random events is a handicap common to all architects.* As if in explanation, Smith read from a newspaper article that had no date: *Against his doctor's orders, on August 27, 1965*, the article begins, *Le Corbusier went for a swim in the Mediterranean Sea at Roquebrune-Cap-Martin, France. Bathers found his body on the beach and he was pronounced dead at 11 a.m. It was assumed that he may have suffered a heart attack and drowned. The drowning took place in view of E1027 the house built by Eileen Gray in 1929.* Walking through the house fifty years after the drowning, the journalist described in great detail what remained of the original interior. *For Gray, a dwelling should be a living organism not an obsession with hygiene or codes, made of the atmosphere required by inner life.* On the rooftop where she could look down on the sea where Corbusier drowned, the journalist carried on through a glass enclosure for a spiral stair, a delicate work of steel and glass, where she could not tell if she was climbing or falling through light and air, *it was like being in a film,* she writes, *connecting and disconnecting continuously, building up and breaking down. I never wished to leave.*

Smith talked for a while longer before he stopped and turned on a projector. Smith appeared on the screen. I don't know if the other Smith disappeared or if I couldn't see him because he was sitting next to me. It may be the case that he and Smith were in fact talking to one another and that I was in the film. Smith, it turned out, had made a number of films, more like diary-entries than something you would see in a cinema. One was of different skies, birds flying, broken cloud, aeroplanes cutting across empty space like pencil lines. Another is of children playing, crashing imaginary machines. In one he recorded a huge moon reflected in Lake Mali; according to his notes the film runs for an entire night, tracing the moon as it moved across the surface of the earth. He called it a self-portrait, a reference, I can only assume, to his own face which, according to those who knew him, was ghostly pale. Locals said he was the whitest white man they had ever seen. As white, I once thought, as Hart Crane in a picture taken by Walker Evans months before Crane fell from the stern of the Orizaba three hundred miles north of Havana and disappeared without trace.

In any case, I have not seen the films and only know them indirectly as they are described, quite discreetly, in Smith's notes. As far as I know, Smith did not show his films to anybody while he was alive. *Films*, he writes, *are a kind of mirror that does not reflect the world in the way people might expect but breaks the world up; fragments what might be real into any number of broken versions of itself. There is a scene at the beginning of one of Nabokov's Russian novels*, Smith writes, *where the narrator observes furniture being delivered to a house across the street. Objects from an old life are transported, before his eyes, into one that is new. The onlooker is mesmerised for a time by a mirror as removal men carry a dresser between parked cars beneath the city trees across which passed a flawlessly clear reflection of boughs sliding and swaying, not arboreally, but with a human vacillation, produced by the nature of those who were carrying this sky, these boughs, this gliding facade.* Perhaps this was why Smith did not want his films to be seen before he was gone. Not until *then*, or until *after* then, when there would be no going back, could the films pass across the immeasurable spaces hidden in that *human vacillation* – the briefest crossing, movement or thought. Instead I was left to meet with Smith in my drugged unconscious, one of those dark rooms, tombs or temples, where we go to meet the dead.

At the close of the same dream, or one very much like it,

Smith switched off the projector and looked at me. We were on a small white boat in the middle of the sea. *Let me tell you a secret*, Smith said. *I did not write any of it. It was written by a ghost, a form of spirit, a man or a woman who, at night, inhabits my body. I employ a number of devices*, Smith said looking at the waves, *in order for the transfer – or transformation – to take place. This is generally pleasurable compared with the alternatives. She comes into my body and I am no longer present. She writes page after page. In the morning I wake and there are the pages stacked neatly on my desk. She even adds my name to make me think what is written there might belong to me. She did not want the stories. But I wanted the stories*, Smith told me in my dream. *I wanted the stories desperately.*

~

It was, I think, no coincidence that I had at that time developed a fierce phobia of the cinema. Sometimes, unable to bring myself to swallow the two yellow-jacketed zopiclone, a name that located the drug in my mind somewhere between Eadweard Muybridge's zoopraxiscope and Edward Smith's zoological theory of collage, I would walk to the Odeon and buy a ticket as if it were the most natural thing in the world. But no matter how many times I went, I could not bring myself to enter the darkness of the auditorium. Instead I found a seat in the brightly lit foyer and drank Coke out of paper cups until the manager came around and told me he was closing for the night. On occasion, I liked to imagine the films I had failed to see and as the audience filed from the screening room looked for any trace of emotion on the faces of those who had witnessed what I had not. Generally, I was shocked to observe, each patron looked no different from whom they had been when they entered and I wondered why they put themselves through it. Occasionally, though, I glimpsed a face I had observed only an hour or so before that had altered completely. In some cases they seemed to have aged, the way faces of those known to me would age after they had been crying uncontrollably. In other cases they appeared much younger, as if they had returned, in that brief passage of time, to their youth. Of course each face would eventually set itself back, but in that brief interval upon exiting from a dark and foreign world each person was for a moment somebody unknown to whom he or she happened to be; or at least that was what I liked to think. And it could be that we had swapped places, somehow, and I was making my way with them into any number of other lives all at once and without fear for whether or not I would return... the way a child follows a butterfly into the woods, unthinking and unafraid.

I had assumed I would be prescribed Nembutal, but barbiturate based tranquilisers had long been banned. I later read of young men and women who travelled to Mexico, where it was used to euthanize pets, to buy lethal doses of Nembutal. After reading these articles, supplemented with pictures of healthy, happy-looking teenagers, I dreamt I too was travelling to Mexico, not to commit suicide but in search of Edward Smith. Sadly, I could only ever find his shadow as he turned a corner ahead of me; I could not get to the end of the alleyway or street in time to see if he was still in sight but his silhouette would linger on the ground like spilled liquid or a burn.

Ana Mendieta, who was killed after falling from a window in New York City in 1985, also travelled to Mexico, and her photographs are the closest likeness to the dream shadows I seemed to be collecting. Smith had made extensive notes on Mendieta's fall and I began to wonder if Smith's writing had taken the place of my dreams. *In the early hours of Sunday September 8ᵗʰ 1985,* Smith writes, *police responded to a call made from an apartment on Mercer Street. A scream had been heard and a woman shouting no. And then what another man, a witness who saw nothing on that dark night, called an* explosion. *Mendieta's body, all but flattened by the impact, was discovered by police on the roof of the Delion Delicatessen, a twenty-four hour grocers selling cut meats, milk and fruit and vegetables. Mendieta had fallen 34 stories,* Smith writes. *It would later be estimated that she was travelling at over 120 miles an hour at the moment of impact and that the fall, given Mendieta's weight and the distance travelled, would have lasted four seconds, which,* writes Smith, *feels like an inordinately long time.* The only other person present when Mendieta fell from the window of 34E Mercer Street was her husband, Carl Andre. When they arrived at the apartment, police noted that Andre had been drinking but that he was calm. The television was on in the sitting room and the bedroom was in a state of disarray. *The windows in the bedroom were open,* Smith writes, *onto the vast architecture of the air that is lower Manhattan in the middle of the night. Goddam,* said officer ___ when he stepped over to the window and looked out on the view. *Before accompanying them to the police station for further questioning,* writes Smith, *Andre gave the police a signed copy of a sculpture catalogue to show them what he did.*

The District Attorney charged the Minimalist sculptor with the murder of Ana Mendieta. As far as the police were concerned there were signs of a struggle, there was no note to suggest Mendieta had taken her own life and the chances of accidental death appeared improbable given that the windows were set high in the wall – at chest height on a grown man – and that Mendieta was 4 feet 10 inches tall. *It was also well known to her friends*, writes Smith, *that Ana Mendieta suffered from a paralysing fear of heights*. At the opening of the trial almost two years after Mendieta's death, Andre waived the right to a jury. The evidence would be weighed by the judge alone, who would be struck by the stoic quietude of the defendant who barely moved except to scratch gently the back of his wrist. According to Smith, who would return again and again to what seem like minor details in the case, there was some disagreement in the build up to the trial concerning the word *expose*. When he called 911 Carl Andre told the operator: *What happened was we had... a quarrel about the fact that I was more exposed to the public realm than she was and she went to the bedroom and I went after her and she went out of the window*. Andre, as was well known at the time, did not like to be photographed. *On the morning after Mendieta's death, faced with a video camera in the police station where he was being held, Andre snapped out of his stupor*, writes Smith, *and asked for a lawyer*. From then on, he told the police that he did not know what happened, he did not see her fall, that he was in the other room. Andre's 911 call is, therefore, the closest recording we have from the time of Mendieta's fall through space – that

140

and the imprint of her body in the roof of the Delion Deli. *As in all cases of a fall it is the missing exposure – the passage between exposures,* Smith writes – *that haunts us; that marks us, most of all.*

Ana's sister, Raquel, who has always maintained, Smith writes, *that it was Mendieta who threatened to expose Andre to the public for adultery and to sue him for divorce, told the DA, that Ana must have challenged him somehow, even though she feared what her husband would do, and that this was what led to the fight and for Ana – in those terrible words* – to go out of the window. *According to her sister and a number of close friends, Ana Mendieta had been collecting evidence of her husband's affairs with other women at the time of her death – letters, bank statements, hotel receipts. She made two sets of photocopies; one was kept in her studio in Rome, the other – which was never found – was in the Mercer Street apartment on the night of her death,* writes Smith. Any reference to divorce was deemed inadmissible in court, however, including the photocopies found or otherwise. Yet in Smith's mind, the absent material came to assume great significance. It was as if Mendieta had carefully placed a final set of works, he writes – a purloined literature in which the object of study – the reason so many of us gather at these shores – would be left lying somewhere between what is written and what can be read.

Born in Cuba, Mendieta was 8 years old when she was exiled to the United States in 1961 along with thousands of other children as part of Operation Peter Pan. From Miami, Ana and her sister were moved to an orphanage in Cedar Rapids where she was raised until she went to art school in

Iowa City. *In many ways*, Smith writes, *the place that Ana Mendieta and her sister had understood to be home would disappear while she was gone.* Her father was arrested and imprisoned in Cuba. Her mother, heart-broken, would eventually follow her daughters to America. *In the midst of this disappearance, which seemed on-going and which would, like all forms of loss, assume many peculiar forms,* Smith writes, *Mendieta worked with earth and fire, water and blood, with gunpowder. She made photographs and films – light exposures – that could fly, so to speak, beyond immediate circumstances, like enchanted emblems, so that much of what she made does not exist in the way that sculpture or paintings otherwise exist. Instead, her works came to occupy a world between what could and could not be evidenced, a terrain we each in someway understand,* writes Smith, *but struggle to describe.*

Mendieta's work was, inevitably, used against her in the trial. But it was the inconsistencies in police evidence – undated photographs of the crime scene, incomplete search warrant applications, the lack of notes taken by detectives leading the case – that undermined the case against Carl Andre. *To that extent,* Smith writes, *Ana Mendieta suffered the same sad fate of any Latino woman found dead and naked in New York City in 1985.* In the end the judge would reach the verdict that the prosecution had not proved beyond reasonable doubt that Carl Andre had murdered Ana Mendieta. This is well known. *And yet this story – like so many stories,* Smith writes – *takes place in what we do not know. It was necessary to reinvent it all,* Ana Mendiata wrote in a poem found among her belongings after her death;

rewrite the ritual. But the photocopies she had collected and stored in secret in New York were never found, the assumption being that Andre had had them destroyed.

For a long time Smith was haunted by a story of the public prosecutor, Elizabeth Lederer, leaving court alone and empty-handed but for the plywood model of 34 E Mercer Street, an exhibit used as evidence against him. Perhaps because the space had been so violently breached, or perhaps because the police photographs of the apartment were sealed forever in a box, the ordinary planes and surfaces of the rooms in which people live their lives seemed to slip and slide in Smith's imagination. Andre told police they had watched TV while drinking champagne and were shocked by the extent to which the forty-year-old re-run, Without Love, paralleled their lives. *A television playing in a room late at night,* writes Smith, *is part of the immediate world of things – furniture, clothes, food, pictures on the wall – and yet it has nothing to do with those things, with what is actually there, offering only a system of collisions where what is completely apparent collides with what is completely gone, and in some ways,* writes Smith, *Carl Andre and Ana Mendieta were characters in a TV show or a dream, inhabiting rooms that shifted according to changes in atmosphere and emotion.* On the night Ana Mendieta and Carl Andre met at the opening of her first solo exhibition in New York, her pictures fell from the walls. Witnesses say it had something to do with the heat but it would not be lost on those who were there to what extent the facts in the case – the fragments of the story – had taken flight. *For one thing,* Smith writes, *Mendieta loved to share her dreams. She once described a dream to her friend, W A,*

143

that he would never forget. She dreamed that Picasso had flown her to New York, taken her everywhere, introduced her to everybody who was anybody, giving her a wonderful time. And when she woke up she heard on the radio that Picasso had died. Perhaps this is why many people still dream of Ana Mendieta after she has gone. It might also be why, writes Smith, *when I think of the 34th floor apartment on Mercer Street, the bedroom window looks for all the world like a movie screen.*

~

In the weeks before he died, Carl Andre was hospitalised with dementia, Smith writes. *Hallucinating and lashing out, he had forgotten who everybody was. In the end,* Smith writes, *Carl Andre admitted to a nurse that he had murdered Ana Mendieta in 1985. The doctors at the hospital said it was not possible to trust what somebody was saying in his condition and it was never reported.*

Either way, it cannot be true. As far as I know, Carl Andre is still alive.

No one can know what happened, writes Smith, *in August 20__, when S. jumped and fell through the air.* I found this sentence, not in one of my dreams, but next to a note on a TV programme showing men and women working on a vast white plain as they drilled hundreds of feet into a glacier with huge pieces of machinery, cutting away long tubes of ice from frozen layers beneath the snow. The deepest layers of ice sediment were formed thousands of years ago. Pulling the ice-rods up to the surface, a dating expert tells the presenter that these long white tubes are memories of the world's atmosphere. But the ice rods, stacked together in an underground lab, reminded me, writes Smith, *of the rods and cones in our eyeballs, seen under a microscope, which allow us to perceive colour. Or the white flecks of paint in a portrait that bring the sitter's eyes to life.* On the following page, and in a hand-written passage that seemed somehow related in my mind, Smith describes a dream in which he watches S. walking in the snow. *It was as if S. was walking across an empty page*, writes Smith. Suddenly he wasn't there anymore. Then, in his shaky hand: *Dream – alone.*

For a long time I assumed Smith used the letter S. in his writings to represent himself. S. cannot work. S. naked by the window. S. lost again. Etcetera. By describing himself in the third person, it was as if he intended to appear and disappear at once, or so I told myself, and I automatically translated the S. into an *I* if I happened to be copying out passages either from the text or from memory. In doing so, the S written over and over again – now straightened, as it were, into an *I*, or maybe rounded into the *0* of an *eye* – began to remind me of the criminal philology of Edward Rulloff. Only later did I begin to wonder if Smith was not in fact referring to himself but to a name he couldn't bring himself to write and that each of these isolated sounds, cut loose and alone, referred to the same person Catherine had mentioned when she gave me Smith's book. Perhaps this was why I began to think that Edward Smith was of the belief that names were not arbitrary but connected in some mysterious way like a set of pathways leading to a world of ghosts. Then, after reading a long passage describing the huge assemblage of interlinking lines of a sculpture made by Tony Smith – with the title, Smoke, of all things – fabricated in Los Angeles some forty years after the sculptor's death, I realised that the only reason Edward Smith showed any interest in the work is because the two men share the same name.

The same can be said of the traveller, mountain climber, surgeon, novelist, and showman, Albert Smith, who in 1855 was one of the most famous men in the world, known best for his stage shows reproducing in absurd detail his travels through Europe, Asia and the Middle East. The most notorious of these, Ascent of Mont Blanc, merged dramatic painted backdrops, a real Swiss chalet, St. Bernard dogs padding the aisles, witty songs accompanied at the piano and amusing patter where Smith adopted the dress, manners and accents of tourists, inn-keepers and mountain guides met along the way. Smith packed the Egyptian Hall, Piccadilly, for six nights a week plus matinées, giving 2,000 performances in all, piling fortune upon fame. *Yet nowadays*, Smith writes, *Albert Smith is all but forgotten. It is as if he fell into a snow filled ravine whilst climbing his beloved White Mountain never to be seen or heard of again.* Caught in a blizzard of his own, Smith appears to confuse Albert Smith who conquered the Alps in 1850 with George Albert Smith, the early film pioneer and hypnotist who helped establish the Society for Psychical Research. *George Albert Smith proved on many occasions that it was possible,* writes Smith, *to communicate using the mind and to take control of another person with means of suggestion and tricks of light and dark.*

For the same reason, there is an extended digression describing Patti Smith's fall from a stage during a concert in Tampa in 1977. *Smith, Smith, Smith*, writes Edward Smith, *the name of a person who has no name. How many men and women have checked into hotel rooms under the same alias, Smith writes, hoping to be other people for the night?*

Smith's concern with names did not end there. Through his window at the hotel in Montreaux, Smith could identify each of the peaks that rose like arrows against the sky. And for Smith the names given to natural phenomena seemed to take on a personal significance. Mountains and rivers. Lakes and trees. Wildflowers that grew in the summer and spring: aquilegia, columbine, Linaria, Edelweiss, tiger lily, phlox. He made a note of them as he walked, observing that the world is named into existence. *But of course,* he writes, *the opposite is also the case.* And I wondered if Smith dreamed of other worlds, dusk lands, made from other names, designations he could not bring himself to write. For hours on end Smith gazed at the mountains. *If you put a word onto a mountain – like in the hills of California*, Smith writes, *there is a special kind of erasure because the word transforms into a picture and it is not clear if one is seeing what one reads or reading what one sees. Whether it was paintings, or movies, or towns*, Smith writes, *the phrase Going to the Mountains has, ever since Cezanne, been synonymous with making pictures – with cancelling out what is real.* Serge Eisenstein frequently visited a rollercoaster in Los Angeles that went by the name of American Mountains. It was, he said, the greatest kind of film. Hokusai saw Mount Fuji in his dreams and painted it again and again so that it would never be out of sight. *My favourite mountain picture is a collage Humphrey Jennings made in 1933*, writes Smith, *in which a giant Swiss roll floats in front of a photograph of the Alps, like the scene outside my window. Even as it reveals the melancholy of collage, I laugh out loud whenever I see it*, writes Smith.

Perhaps this is why, for the first few weeks of his time in Montreux, Smith could not face the Alpine hills and paths behind the hotel directly. Instead, he walked the town in the evening when the night sky all but wiped out the view collecting postcards and tourist brochures promoting local mountain scenes. He lined the walls of his room with these images where he took all of his meals, washed himself and where he wrote page after page in pencil and pen. Great mountain scenes began to form in his mind resembling not the world outside but some vast Victorian Diorama, one with a name of its own. His hallucinations took on the form of a mental geology – *mountain ranges tracing those ancient cracks and faultiness of the surface of our planet, formed,* Smith writes, *in a time of crushing and expanding heat, as warped and contorted sediment pushed to the surface out of*

ocean basins laying waste to everything in its midst. Volcanic explosions, earthquakes, avalanches, dense clouds of toxic dust a thousand miles wide. The origins of our world, writes Smith, *and what is left of it – is the same ripping and cutting and pasting. That must be why collage,* writes Smith, *is the language of the lost. It is not just the transporting of pictures from one place to another, but also words, names, like birds in cages and lions in zoos, are ripped from one world and dropped, without warning into another fabricated landscape made to resemble, not the reality they once knew, but an environment based on nothing but a picture from a book. Collage* is *our natural world,* writes Smith.

~

One morning, after leaving Eleanor's café and walking through the night, the sun rose early and I realised it was summer. On entering my room I stopped. The windows, which I habitually left open, were closed and the smell of cigarette smoke hung in the air. I checked the bathroom and then went to the bed. My chair was turned away from the desk and, as I scanned the room, it occurred to me someone had been waiting there while I was out. Smith's papers were where I had left them but something had changed. Some months before, my notes were open in a similar fashion. On seeing the same word written over and over again, my daughter, who now seemed like a survivor to me and who was at the time learning to write, decided to copy her own version of *Smith*. I found the name that my daughter had written, as I sat back down in my room, looking about me for extinguished cigarettes, as if it had been placed on purpose, among a collection of coastal photographs showing erosion of the deranged folds in the rock – evidence of how the world was made and how it would one day disappear – flying up from the ground and back towards the earth. I was struck by the extent to which the handwritten letters, *S m i t h*, resembled the undulating sediment. Back then, my daughter's words were still very much like pictures but before long that would change and I remember wondering if, in doing so, she was becoming lost to herself or if it was the case that her picture words were opening up new routes to a self that would be inexhaustible. Seeing her handwriting in the early yellow light I felt a longing I had not experienced for some time.

I picked up my jacket and went out into the hall, making sure as I did so, to turn my key in the lock. I was surprised when I reached the street to see Catherine passing by. I waved but she did not see me as she crossed onto the main road already filling with traffic. I wondered what she was doing there and, then, why she had been in my room. I jogged after her. Perhaps she had news about Edward Smith. But as I reached the crossing the lights changed and I was held up by a surge of heavy trucks. I followed on the other side of the road and it occurred to me this was the first time I had seen Catherine outside of her rooms overlooking the park. It was difficult to keep up. Catherine had quickened her pace and I all but ran to the junction only in time to see her turn into an alleyway and out of sight. An eternity passed before the lights changed and I could cross with the other early walkers between cars and trucks to the end of a parade of shops and the alleyway where they kept their bins.

Catherine was gone. I ran along the passage to the next main road then, having all but given up hope, saw Catherine on the pavement opposite. She looked like she was waiting for someone. When I waved she turned once more and continued into a residential street. This time, I crossed without care for the cars, one of which pulled up just short of me. I could still hear the sound of horns as I ran into the next road where Catherine was reaching into her purse and turning into one of the leafy front gardens that lined the street. I stopped at the gate. With her key in the lock, she looked at me. It was some time before I realised I was not looking at Catherine L. I stood back. The door closed and she was gone.

Beset by tiredness and despair, I moved on without thinking. When I came to my senses I realised I was back at Eleanor's cafe. I reached for the door but it was locked. I assumed it was earlier than I thought. Wondering whether I might wait, I saw that the windows were boarded and the sign had been taken down. A security notice had been fixed to one of the boards. The sudden closure left me in shock. I thought back to the previous evening. I had read and made notes as always; Eleanor brought out plates and cleaned glasses; she joked with regulars; people came and went. On occasion I looked up at the white suspension bridge and standing in the street it occurred to me then that I would never discover where the picture was from. Before leaving, I peered in at a gap in the newspaper sealing the door hoping for one last look at the room. Only when I was back at my desk, surrounded by my notes, did I realise that the newspaper pages were over two years out of date.

In the last few days before he disappeared Edward Smith

had been seen in a café in Montreux writing as if in a fever. *I looked across the street*, Smith writes, *for a moment I saw mountains and a white river gleaming in the sun.* He watched as fish jumped in the light. He closed his eyes and tried to hear what was happening. When he opened them again he focused on a young man standing in the sunlight. He had thick lips and a flat nose and his short fair hair curled in tight-knots barely covering his sunburned scalp. No more than a boy, he said things about truth and what was to come. *Pacing on the spot, lifting his face and dropping it again as tourists made their way up and down the pavement, the young man had chosen on that warm September afternoon*, Smith writes, *to stand out of the shade cast by the opposite rooftops.* Slowly, his movements intensified. Small short gestures, building up into wider sweeping movements of his arms, hands and wrists, his knees bending, his waist thrusting into the street and then back toward the wall, sweat beading on his forehead. But not once at any point did he open his eyes. Was he blind or was he protecting himself from the glare of the sun? Either way, Smith could not help noticing that while the boy did not wish to see, his greatest desire, beyond all else, was to be seen. *I think I watched that boy for an hour*, writes Smith, *but I may just as likely have glimpsed him as I was walking by.*

For a long time after the encounter, Smith appears to have been unable to write. It is not clear if the evangelist's robotic movements cast some kind of spell on the unwitting observer who had felt not an ounce of sympathy for a man who was clearly out of his wits.

Of course, Smith later confessed, *in those bizarre*

movements and empty words I also saw myself, or the version
of myself I see in mirrors or in dreams. But there is nothing
so unusual about that. During the following weeks, as his
paralysis took a firmer grip on his waking efforts to put
something, anything, down on paper, his thoughts flew again
in the direction of the young man in the sun whose image now
formed the impression, he suddenly realised, of a ghost. Smith
never saw him again. *For all I know he fell in the street from
exhaustion and was carried away to a hospital or an asylum
or a church*, he writes. *But I see his face when I close my eyes
and I realise now the boy looked exactly like S.* It was
suddenly painful for Smith to think that if S. did come back –
which was impossible – he might not recognise him. *I am
writing less and less these days*, writes Smith in one of his final
notes. Choosing instead to watch, to stand guard for the next
time. When the birds come onto my balcony, writes Smith, I
wonder if that is him.

On one of my visits to her rooms the Autumn before,
Catherine asked me, quite out of the blue, if I had any
memories that were important to me. I told her I didn't know
what she meant. *You know*, she said, *something from the past
that you don't want to forget*. I looked down into the park
but there was nobody there. *I remember getting lost, I said.
On a heath near the sea. I walked endlessly as it got later and
later and I didn't think I would ever get off that heath. To
this day, I don't know how I did. I used to think I must have
found a sign or another walker showed me the way. But then
I remembered I was carrying a drawing of a spiral – a
beautiful spiral shell. Something my daughter had made. It
was meant to be a snail. I don't know how it helped me get*

off the heath. I've all but lost the memory now. But I've kept the drawing, in case I should ever need a map. Catherine looked at me. *Your daughter?* I nodded. *It was a long time ago*, I said. Catherine sat back and lit a cigarette. She looked at me for a long time. *Will you show me the drawing?* I watched her through the smoke. *Yes*, I said. But I knew I never would.

~

After a series of particularly bad dreams where one violent picture overlapped with the next, I realised the pictures in my head were not changing places with each other but that I was changing places with the pictures. I decided then I had to leave Edward Smith behind.

I walked south from where I was staying and in the autumn sunshine was soon of the feeling that I had walked too far. Archway Bridge loomed in front of me like a gate through which whole armies were meant to pass, invading giants, or gods abandoning their posts. Edward Smith had passed this way before and I wondered, in despair, to what extent it was ever possible for people to make their own way in places such as these.

The original Archway Bridge, writes Smith, *was demolished at the end of the Nineteenth Century. Whenever I happen to be passing that way the destroyed version flashes before my eyes as if the past and its transient structures were impossible to escape. The lost bridge built in brick and stone and intended to stand for as long as Saint Paul's, links in my mind with Rodin's gateway to hell*, writes Smith. *Not the glossy black reproductions in books and museums around the world but the original plaster work – standing at 4 meters high 3 meters wide and one meter deep – from which each subsequent bronze was cast. In the whiteness of the plaster the central void takes on the appearance of a mist – the fog from which each soul is formed and to which it will return like a great cloud upon the sea. It is possible to focus on the bodies twisted perpetually into the forms of anguish and pain but I only see what is lost: the great space around which the sculpture is nothing but a frame for those indeterminate figures reaching back and forth across a terrible, visceral screen.* Here Smith attached a handwritten note which is perhaps the closest he came to describing the person Catherine mentioned to me.

Last summer my friend, whom I had known since we were at school, drove his motorbike west from his home on Belsize Road to Camden Town. There he turned north along Havestock High Street before crossing the Heath over the Spaniard's Way and up to Highgate Hill. In this manner, he snaked slowly on his customised Honda, through the city following the shape, I now realise, of an S. At daybreak he arrived unnoticed at Hornsey Lane where the narrow carriageway crosses Archway Road via the suspension bridge high in the air above. My friend was not tall, at six foot I stood a head taller than him by the time we finished school, but he was a lean, well built man and it would not have been difficult for him to climb the black railings that line the bridge and throw himself to his death over one hundred feet below the way he did that morning in July.

I write these things, Smith writes, *but I was not there. I had left the city the Autumn before and I had no intention of returning. I was not invited to a funeral and there are no records, as far as I have found, to say what happened on that day. It was as if he disappeared without trace, while the city carried on. And yet whenever I think of him I see this picture like a photo cut from a book or a magazine. Or a still from a film. He is standing on the bridge, in this picture. Looking down and waving to somebody far below.*

I looked away. Smith had brought me to a place I couldn't bear and I was strangely grateful. *Before he fell*, Smith writes, *S. survived several overdoses* and I looked at the handful of yellow pills I carried with me almost automatically. But I did not swallow them or throw them away. I put them in my pocket and started walking once more. Halfway between Archway and Angel I passed the cinema, swallowing people into its darkness, it seemed to me, as they queued at its doors and I was struck by a terrible vertigo. For a moment I could not see. I was overcome with the feeling that I was suspended in mid-air like a word in the middle of a page without any connection with what could be recovered except as an endless movement away from itself. Perhaps this was the nausea Paul Klee had intended to describe in the shaky outlines of *his* Angel. *Klee's Angel, fallen not out of heaven but from history, would like to stay*, writes Smith, *awaken the dead, and make whole what has been smashed. But a storm is blowing from paradise.*

I felt myself beginning to black out and groped about for somewhere to rest. Out of that void words returned to me as an echo that had almost faded away – final fragments from the writings of Edward Smith: *Without realising it, writes Smith, I have for a long time been haunted by Bruegel's painting of a Landscape with the Fall of Icarus. Icarus' tragedy is not that he failed to fly higher than the sun but that nobody saw him fall. The great galleon, caught in a fair wind, passes by, the sailors in its rigging bent on lowering their final sail. In the fields the ploughman ploughs, at the shore, the fisherman dreams of fish. The partridge, flightless upon its perch, has its mind on other things too. Everything and everyone – the shepherd included, legs twisted beneath him – turns away from the disaster. Even the painter*, writes Smith, *forever absent from the scene, does not catch Icarus, as it were, in mid-air – neither in one place or the other – but shows only his pale left leg pointing back at the sky – a strange form of signal – from out of the water where he will drown.* How hard it is, the picture seems to say, to forgive ourselves. *What makes things worse*, writes Smith, *is that in all likelihood the picture, which has hung in the Musée des Beaux Arts in Brussels since 1912, is not in fact a picture painted by Bruegel. It is probably a copy made by an unknown artist of another work that was either lost or destroyed. At best the composition – the ploughman on the left, the boat hard right, the sun high and central – could be said to have been Bruegel's invention but even that isn't certain. Instead of the moment there is,* Smith writes, *wreckage upon wreckage. What are these, pictures, words, objects,* writes Smith, *that arrive from nowhere as if out of a field of white mist, there for a time and then gone? Just like them, I am neither here nor there,* writes Smith. *I am lost.*

He stared at the shaky black lines. Before too long, Edward Smith laced on the boots he had bought that morning and walked out into the snow.

Three

Shoot Shoot Shoot, or A Case of Mistaken Identity

He had to prove somehow the reality of his own footprint there being nobody else who could.

Robert Creeley, *The Island*

The September before last, I travelled to Cluj-Napoca, a city I did not know, hoping that a change of place would help me escape the sleeplessness and depression of grief. For many years I had wanted to re-trace the footsteps of Paul Sharits, who had travelled to Romania in 1978 to film Brancusi's sculpture garden in Targu Jiu.

I caught an early flight, the half-empty plane lifting into the clearing skies above London's northern satellite towns just as the dawning shapes of houses and trees could be made out from the gloom of night. I remembered something I had read about the circles of stones dotted around the English countryside, pointing accusingly at the sky from where celestial eyes, one presumes, could gaze down upon so many human clocks. At some point our ties with these ancestors were broken. It's not that we do not know what the stone circles are meant to represent, the writer suggested, but that we cannot remember.

As the plane levelled out I moved to another seat away from the window and buckled the belt in my lap. The sight of these first shapes resolving into familiar forms was still playing on my mind as we touched down on a runway to the south of a grey line of hills marking the start of the mountains that once separated Transylvania from the rest of the Hungarian Empire.

In the baggage hall there was an unexplained delay. We waited over an hour in a room without windows and too few seats. I sat on the ground with my back to the wall gazing at a small child half asleep in her mother's lap. I slept momentarily and woke with a start wondering what had happened. The child was watching me and the third memory

I had stored returned to me suddenly. As I recalled the weight in my arms of our dead baby, deposited as it were in the deepest chambers of my heart, I thought of everything that I must have forgotten in order to continue this dream of myself. While I can remember how heavy she felt, a weight that corresponded to nothing else I had ever carried or held, I could not remember if our baby's skin was warm or cold or if her fingers could be curled around my thumb or if they had already begun to stiffen in the air of the hospital room as the rain poured down outside. And I questioned to what extent the memories I had locked up in this way had come to take the place of events, so that I was remembering a memory and not what had hit Anne and I that day and night tearing us apart.

I looked up. Nothing had changed. As my eyes adjusted I saw a man in a heavy yellow ski-jacket walking toward me. Most people in the room were in shirtsleeves, their overcoats and belongings piled beside them on the floor like the last of an abandoned race. Just then the baggage carousel jumped into life, the crowd rose as one, and I lost sight of the man. I collected my bag and made my way to the exit looking over my shoulder as I went.

It was good to get outside. The air was warm, fragrant with the end of summer. I climbed into an ancient taxicab while those ahead of me disappeared into newer German models. *English?* the driver asked as we pulled away, his mouth hidden by a heavy white moustache. I told him this was my first time in Romania. *You're not in Romania*, he said. His eyes twinkled. He wore no seatbelt and worked the car as if he were sitting in his garden surrounded by plants tended by him for years on end or in his study flanked by books he had read many times over.

The road ran in an endlessly straight line, drawn by some obsessive hand, from the airport into the city of Cluj. Small housing settlements broken up by barren farmland dotted the landscape before high-rise housing blocks shot up into the sky. The traffic slowed into a dense line of vehicles and we crept toward the centre of a bustling city. Where factories had once stood, according to the cab driver, there were office blocks and glass shopping arcades. *What do they make?* he asked me. *We used to make the greatest beer in the world. Now the beer is full of chemicals. I don't drink it anymore.* I watched as people moved in a frenzy of lunchtime panic. Soon the whole world would look like this. *There are two things you must do while you are in Cluj*, he told me, as we turned into the main square. *You must drink Tuica and you must visit the Hungarian Opera. In London the opera is expensive. Here it is cheap,* he said. *Anyone can go.* He seemed excited by this idea. I told him I liked the movies. In truth I hadn't been into a cinema for some time. I often thought about the darkness into which I had at one time wished to dissolve: I would do this by looking for details at the edge of the frame, a movement, a face, a set of colours that were otherwise invisible, anonymous fragments in the gloom, possessed of a strange semblance, having nothing to do with what, if anything, was unfolding on the screen. In 1978, Paul Sharits told an interviewer who asked him about one of his stroboscopic films, *if you look closely you can see an image of a chair falling over backwards without any apparent reason.* To this day I have never seen the chair. *Cinema is okay*, my driver said as we came into view of the Orthodox Cathedral facing the main Catholic Church, *but opera is life*. It turned out that his girlfriend was appearing that night in the new Wagner production. *There will be a huge party*, he told me. We arrived somewhat suddenly. I paid and we shook hands. *See you at the gala*, he said and drove away. I watched his car disappear around a bend as if into another world. I knew I would never see him again.

I crossed the square to a bar I had spotted from the taxicab and took a table in the corner where I began to work through my notes. Among my papers was a copy of David Lewis' small book on Constantin Brancusi. The book contained pictures of Brancusi at work in his studio as well as examples of his stone and metal sculptures carefully set in front of a black screen. Here you could make out patterns repeating across an empty void, each form appearing out of nowhere, or so it would seem. Perhaps this was what Ad Reinhardt had been attempting to paint when he died in 1967, a solemn background for everything that was lost, for what would otherwise remain invisible. By way of contrast, the book included a reproduction, taken from Brancusi's own collection, of a woodcarving by Ferdinand Hodler. *Saw in hand*, the author writes, *the old*

carpenter suddenly stops work. He stares into the distance, beyond the physical confines of his workshop, deep in thought and stroking his beard. It is the portrayal of an epiphany, the writer goes on, *the realisation of the relationship between birth and death, between childhood and old age. Here is the artisan who has acquired knowledge about eternity and human existence through the direct, solitary and one-to-one experience of his materials and craft.* I studied the image carefully. The carpenter was halfway through building a coffin for a child.

Weary from reading, I searched through my bag for a pen. I knew at some stage I would have to write something – a postcard or letter – explaining where I was but I had no idea where to begin. Looking up, as if expecting the bar to offer guidance on the matter I noticed the man in the yellow jacket I had seen at the airport. Heavyset and dark-haired, he sat with his back to me, in conversation with the barman who appeared to know him well. I watched the barman nodding, then he leaned across the bar and pointed in my direction. I collected my things, laid some money on the table and left.

Walking through the busy streets of Cluj, I felt as if I had returned to a place I knew well. This was of course quite impossible and yet I half expected to come upon a message I had left myself on some previous visit. In time the streets narrowed and I slowed my pace. With some relief I realised I was lost. I stopped and looked back the way I had come. There were no markers or entranceways only an unending grey façade lining either side of the cobbled alleyway that served as access for the major routes at either end. It didn't matter which way I walked. There was no future and the past was lost. I have no way of knowing how long I stood in that street but I realised then it was harder to give up than it was to carry on.

The Hotel Sebastopol was nothing like its name. I took a first floor room where I planned to write; something I had found impossible during the previous months in England. I put my jacket over the mirror and surveyed the room: a single bed against one wall was flanked by a small dressing table; on the facing wall an enormous television had been mounted where once there might have been a watercolour depicting the nearby hills or the river Someşul Mic daubed by some forgotten hand. I ran a glass of water, sat on the bed and flicked on the television. An English news channel was showing pictures of a boat listing hopelessly in the waves. I couldn't get the sound to work and watched for a while as the camera zoomed in on the faces of men and women packed into the flimsy craft. The report cut to a journalist standing on a beach framed by an impossibly blue ocean. The boat seemed to have been swallowed by a much larger ship. Marines looked down on their new cargo, their heads bare, surgical masks over their noses and mouths. Everyone looked afraid. This silent gobbling up of the lost left me with a sense of unease. I turned off the TV and reached for the pad of paper lying next to the telephone headed with the Hotel's name and address.

For some minutes I sat in silence thinking about the letter I knew I should write. A series of pictures moved through my mind but I realised I could find no way of connecting where I was with where I had been, as if the order of a person's life could only be set down or worked out incoherently, by accident, and in the knowledge that the little of what might be recorded or said would fail to correspond, except indirectly, with the life that person was living through. I put down the pen and returned to the lobby where I told the receptionist the room was fine. Hoping to find the name of the alley where I had lost my way I asked for a city map but it was impossible to be sure which line on the map corresponded with the place where I had been. Turning to go I caught sight once again of the yellow-jacketed man, disappearing into a stairwell. I waited a few moments, folded away my map and returned to the room for my bag and the notepad where I had written two words: Dear Anne. I tore off the top page and folded it away in my shirt. I checked out of the Hotel Sebastopol where the receptionist insisted I pay for the night's accommodation.

Back in the street I cut a path west along Strada V Fulicia before turning south into Strada E Isac and then east along a central boulevard, past the Museum of Transylvanian Ethnology and the Cathedral. It was beginning to rain. Thinking I had gone far enough I checked behind me before ducking into the lobby of another hotel. The receptionist there, whose face I cannot recall, told me I was in luck. They had something suitable. He handed me a key and I all but ran up the stairs. On entering I was alarmed to find an exact replica of the room I had abandoned less than an hour before. I considered looking for another room or even a different hotel but the whole pursuit had tired me out. I lay on the bed fully clothed and wondered what I would do with myself. I wasn't used to having time or being left alone. My thoughts turned to work.

Every summer Constantin Brancusi would disappear into the forests south of Paris where he would go unseen for weeks on end. During one of these mysterious sojourns he fell from a tree and broke his leg so that he could not stand. For two days he suffered atrociously until a hunter discovered him and managed to take the sculptor to the nearest hospital. Sometime later, Brancusi described the moment he realised he would die alone and helpless on the forest floor. He suddenly remembered what he identified as *The toad's call in the serpent's fangs*. Brancusi made the same cry himself and was soon discovered, as if by some miracle of chance, by the man who saved his life. Through the open window of that hotel room in Cluj, I thought I heard the sound Brancusi described and I listened intently for it again. I lay that way all night – too tired to sleep – listening to the darkness, waiting for a sound I would never hear.

After breakfast, I was due to meet my contact at the university housed in a small medieval building on Corvin Matei but she had called ahead to say she was delayed. The day yawned ahead of me. With the vague intention of visiting the botanical gardens I drifted east along Strada Avram Iancu until I found myself at the gates of the Cemetery of Heroes. On entering, I was greeted with a flash of red and black as a tiny bird, startled by my approach, disappeared into a tree. Wooded with oak, ash and pine, the cemetery was cool and quiet compared with the busy ring road beyond the gate. Walking the narrow paths I studied the tall wooden forms adorning many of the graves and read the names on stones dating back over three hundred years. Approaching one corner where the graves were very old and dishevelled, the quiet that was everywhere seemed to have concentrated into a low drone. The sound became overwhelming. Looking up I saw thousands of bees at work in ivy flowering in dense clumps around the trunk of an ancient tree. Leaving the bees behind I observed a party of mourners slowly ascending the steep central path to where a hearse was waiting, its engine running as if the driver had somewhere to be. Suddenly tired, I rested on one of the many benches constructed, it seemed, as a part of each tomb. The mourners hung back as a man and a woman led the party up the hill. She clasped a bunch of flowers; his hands hung empty at his sides. Earlier that summer, Anne and I had walked to a far corner of a large cemetery on the outskirts of London to a patch of graves dug in neat rows between the railway line and the kennels. We came upon a woman sitting beside a half-filled grave as if she meant to climb into the hole. Two gravediggers waited beside a mound of earth. I stopped. Anne walked over to the woman and touched her shoulder. She said something and pointed to

a patch of earth nearby. The woman stood up and they embraced. I stood in the shade of a large oak and listened to the dogs.

That evening there was a message in my room. I was to meet with the President of the University at 8pm in a nearby restaurant. When I arrived, I was led through a packed and noisy dining hall to a small backroom where the president sat behind a round table, surrounded by colleagues all of whom stopped speaking as I entered. Seeing this huge man encased by the thick stonewalls of the restaurant, I was reminded of a bear in its cave. *Please sit*, the president said. *We have been expecting you.* He continued conversations, it seemed, in several directions at once. Breads and various country dishes were laid out in front of me. *He looks hungry*, the president laughed as local wine was brought and our glasses were filled. He told us he had just returned from the mountains where he owns a cabin close to a lake. One morning he went outside to smoke a cigarette. It had been raining but the day was already warm. *Then bang! I was thrown off my feet and found myself looking up into a cloudless sky!* The president had been hit, as he put it, by a thunderbolt. The ground beneath his feet turned white – *vaporised*, he said. In that instant there was no space between sound and light. *Well, what did you learn from this experience – from this divine intervention?* A professor of historiography asked, finishing his drink. *Absolutely nothing*, the president laughed. *I didn't feel a thing.*

Later, as those around me began to leave, wishing me luck while they disappeared through a low opening back into the main restaurant, the president poured us both plum brandies. Now, it seemed, we could talk. He wanted to know why I was there. I told him about the film Paul Sharits had made in Romania in 1978 and he seemed curious. I told him it was a strange work. Over time, I had come to wonder whether the film existed at all. I had only ever seen a bad copy showing what looked like two films running on top of each other. As far as I could tell the films were identical but one ran less than a second behind the other creating a strange visual echo. It recorded the journey Paul Sharits made from Ljubljana to Bucharest from where he travelled by train to the sculpture garden in Târgu Jiu built by Brancusi in 1937. Glimpses of countryside, cars, busses, trees, and the stones set by Brancusi in the open ground would flash past only to reappear just as they had gone, trapped, or so it seemed, in a zone of memory at the edge of what was present. I told him it was like falling through a dream.

The president of the university listened to me carefully and with some patience. We toasted the journey. Then he told me I had come to the wrong place. Brancusi had lived in Paris all his life, he said, and my travelling filmmaker was an American. He was joking but I knew he was right. We like to say we are following in the footsteps of other people when we travel in this way – to foreign lands – but that can never be the case. Who do we haunt but ourselves?

Just then, Maria, my contact, burst into the room: a robust, tough looking woman who behaved as if something serious had just happened or was about to take place, as if there was no other way for life to be lived. Flustered, she greeted the president warmly. She apologised for missing me earlier in the day. A storm had grounded her flight out of Bucharest, a city she hated. I told her I would like to visit

Bucharest. *If you have no choice*, she said, shrugging. *The only people who have any fondness for the city are those who live in Bucharest. The people are unbearable*, she said. *Like the place. They argue. They rush around. There is no peace. Much better you are in Cluj!*

While he was in Bucharest in 1978 Paul Sharits narrowly escaped being hit by a bus. He had been drinking heavily with locals and was robbed by a woman he had taken back to his room. *That city left a hole in me* he later joked. *I am a collector of holes. Sometimes I think I if I stand up you'll be able to see right through*.

When do you go to Targu-Jiu? Maria asked me. I told her the president of the university had arranged for a car to pick me up at 8am. *Well*, she said. *Good. Then that is that.*

It took Paul Sharits six years to finish his film about the journey to Târgu Jiu, during a particularly difficult period in his life. At midday, on Friday August 6th, 1982 Paul Sharits was shot at point blank range in a bar on Fillmore Avenue in Buffalo, New York. As with any event in the life of an artist, it is difficult to know what to do – if anything – with this biographical detail, the kind that comes to light most commonly in newspaper obituaries; whether the gunshot should accompany us, as it were, into the hallucinatory final films he made before his death in 1993, like a puncture in the unstoppable flow of time; or whether there can be any connection real or otherwise between what happens to a person and the things they make. Yet, there are times when the stories left behind by the lives of others seem to weave with the patterns our own lives form so that it is difficult to understand, it seems to me, one without the other.

The Buffalo News/Wednesday, July 14, 1993 Page C-7

OBITUARIES

Paul J. Sharits, 50, dies; avant-garde filmmaker

The art community is mourning the death of Paul J. Sharits, 50, an internationally acclaimed avant-garde filmmaker and a professor of film at the University at Buffalo for nearly 20 years.

He died unexpectedly Thursday (July 8, 1993) in his home on Buffalo's West Side.

A memorial service is planned at a time to be announced this fall at the Whitney Museum of American Art in New York City, where his work currently is part of an exhibit on Fluxus, a renegade 1960s art movement that he joined in 1965.

"He was one of the key figures in American avant-garde film," says John Hanhardt, curator of film and video at the Whitney. "He was really an artist working within the medium of film, not in storytelling, but in directly visual ways."

"His main contribution," says Jonas Mekas, director of the Anthology Film Archive in New

Paul J. Sharits

"These two books, still intact, will float in a vibrating pool of blackened (and variously drugged) alcohol: they will gently bang into

According to reports, there were two witnesses to the shooting: the barman, Gerd Auslander, who had his back turned the moment Harry Land fired his gun, and Professor Helen O'Grady, a psychology professor from Buffalo College, who was standing across the street. I can't help being struck by this strange pairing of eyewitnesses (who in truth didn't see anything) standing, as it were, at either end of a telescope. Both gave reports to the police. After going through these statements, which are patchy and at times quite strange, I began to realise that the gaps in what it might be possible to know only appeared to widen. Groping for facts, I seemed to be crossing an ever-expanding terrain, like a range of hills seen in the half-light of morning, and I felt as if I were observing figures in a mist, each one a set of barely perceptible vibrations, faint but irresistible, to be sensed in the skin rather than seen with the eyes. And so that day in 1982, less than a year after the attempted assassination of Ronald Reagan, has remained

Nevertheless, the extreme gestures of his art and his life sometimes landed him in trouble.

In 1990, he was charged with menacing and criminal possession of a weapon after he produced a jackknife as he argued with a motorist whose car was blocking his in a UB parking lot. Sharits pleaded guilty to a lesser charge of disorderly conduct and was fined $100.

In 1976, Sharits was stabbed in the back by a woman during an argument at Delaware Avenue and West Chippewa Street. In 1982, he was mistaken for another man and shot in the stomach by a patron who had been arguing at a Fillmore Avenue tavern.

At the time of his death, he was involved in a lawsuit against UB, which relieved him of his professorship in January 1992 over an angry, rambling telegram he sent

175

all but out of reach, suspended within a series of grey patches, or uncertain after-images, dots and lines, from which I have attempted to make my notes.

The shooting preoccupied me over the months leading up to my journey to Cluj-Napoca. On quiet mornings I sometimes thought I could feel the breeze blowing down Fillmore Avenue that noon in August 1982. A wind, triggered perhaps by a gun going off, that has never ceased to blow but has passed over the lakes and rivers between Buffalo and the New England shore, before making its way across the Atlantic, only to reach me almost forty years later, unaware that I was waiting for anything other than my own painful thoughts to catch up with themselves. Gird Auslander told the police he had cut his hand on the glass he was cleaning when the gun went off. He said he knew both men in the vague way he knew each of the regulars that came into the bar: he knew one as a lunchtime drinker; the other would arrive late when everyone else was getting ready to go home. It was strange to see them at the same time that day. Helen O'Grady told police she saw a tall man with white hair fall through the doors of Jerry's Tavern. He walked several paces then sat down on the curb, reminding her of a stray animal who had run out of places to hide.

Joe Land, formerly Jozef Lengyel, was born in a town not far from Budapest and emigrated to the United States in the late-1960s. After settling in Buffalo, Land worked in kitchens and in sweatshops, he had driven a taxi, and laboured on construction sites across the city. He had a literature degree and hoped to work in a school teaching languages. When the police arrived at the scene they found Land sitting on the pavement. They reported that he was not distressed and that he gave no struggle. *It was like he was pleased to see us*, one of the officers said. Land's arrest inevitably corresponds in my mind with this picture of Sharits taken in Bucharest before he travelled on to Târgu Jiu. The note on the back of the photograph reads: *Me with friend*. Sept. 1978.

The first time I read Land's reply to the question: Is this your gun? I had to stop and read it again. *How would I know?* Land said. How hard it must be, I thought, to confirm ownership of an object which had all but killed another man and I thought of all the murder weapons that are never found, that are abandoned, thrown away, destroyed – proof, if it were needed, that it is the things we think we have possession over that have most possession over us.

It was like being in a film, Land is reported to have said. *Normally my eyesight is not so good*, he goes on. *Cloudy. In one eye I am completely blind. Too much reading when I was a boy, he said. Too much drinking when I was a man.* The

free lawyer wanted to use this with the police. He said it had a bearing on events. But that morning Joe Land could see everything. The world was clear. He looked for a long time at the tree on the corner, the same tree he walked past every day for twenty years. *I had never really seen it*, he said. *Not in the way that I should see things, burnt onto the back of my brains.* For a long time (long enough for neighbours to comment) Land looked at the pine, the only tree for miles around, and thought that he could detect in its image the state of on-going deterioration imperceptible to human sight that defines the existence of all living things. He remembered the great oaks and yews along the boundary lines of the farms around his childhood home, how they maintained their station, outliving everyone he knew. Somehow the cross street in Buffalo joined with a path he used to walk as a child in mid-summer beneath an avenue of chestnut trees, a dirt track that would begin and end with the shadows their high branches cast. In his dreams he would wake to find these trees growing in his room. The bark was dark and damp. He would reach down and pull his hands away as if his limbs belonged to someone else. He had not seen his family for many years, his younger brother who had a limp, his grandfather who played the violin. And he wondered to what extent such separations matured within the body, dark unproductive spaces, into which he might stumble and drown. For a time he thought he could see these darkening pools, that perhaps they did not come from within him, before he realised he was looking at the black spots of his deteriorating vision, the same black spots which would eventually turn him blind.

In the weeks before the shooting on Fillmore Avenue

Land's eyesight worsened and the spots began to crowd his vision. At times he could only see smashed images. The interference was particularly bad in the mornings. Some days he would wake to what looked like hundreds of beetles crawling about the low ceiling of his basement room. He signed off work from a nearby Laundromat where he moved bundles of clothes belonging to strangers from one machine to the next. At first he was fearful, but after awhile he became fascinated by what was happening to him. As his vision cleared through the morning he got dressed and made his way to Jerry's Tavern, where he drank most days. He liked to sit as close as possible to one of the obscured windows and observe what was happening in the street change shape in the glass. He found this restful, as if his approaching blindness was already a part of how he saw the world, and he would try to draw on napkins the black shapes that had become the best part of what he could see. While searching his apartment for evidence and other firearms – there were none – the police came across the drawings, stuffed together in a desk. The drawings bear a strange resemblance to the inkblot test-cards used in the 1920s to diagnose schizophrenia or Henri Michaux's mescaline drawings. In my mind, the blots and swirls morphed with other painted distortions, such as Stubb's study of a dingo made in 1772, based not on what the artist had observed but on verbal descriptions brought back from the colonies of bizarre wild dogs drinking from the rivers of Tasmania; or Durer's Rhinoceros based on the reports of armoured cows with horribly over-sized horns stalking the dark interiors of the Indian sub-continent. Gerd Auslander often watched Land making sketch after sketch.

Land would draw with his eyes closed, guided by the softness of the absorbent paper beneath his fingertips. Sometimes it appeared that his pen was hardly moving, at others he drew frenetically, tearing the surface of each white square. For a long time I thought it was strange that Land closed his eyes to draw the densely shifting shapes, as if he could see them fully only by wiping them out, until Anne reminded me that to draw anything is to look away. (As Franz Kafka once put it: *My stories are a way of shutting my eyes.*)

The last time I slept in England, before my journey to Romania, I dreamt my name was Joseph Land. I could hear my name being called. I crossed the room to a small window where I looked down on a child marking the ground with a stick. She was occupied with writing strange characters from an alphabet I couldn't read before rubbing them out with her foot. In my hands was the air rifle with which I hunted birds as a boy. My mouth kept filling with pellets made of lead. Each time I spat them out finches and siskins fluttered around the room. On hearing another voice, I turned and fired at myself. The sound of the gun caused a huge flash of light. When I woke it was the middle of the night and I knew I would not get back to sleep. While on trial, Joe Land told the court in Buffalo he thought Sharits was somebody else. When prosecutors pushed him on who that might be, he told them he had mistaken Sharits for Jozef Lengyel, the man Land had been before he moved to America. He was sent to Buffalo State Psychiatric Centre on the site of the Richardson Olmstead Complex where he remains today.

I had been awake for hours when the car that was to take me to Târgu Jiu pulled up in front of the hotel. For a long time I gazed out of the window, watching the sun rise. Across the street, between two grey buildings, I could see into a walled courtyard. For whatever reason, I found myself transfixed by a narrow corner, empty except for a perfectly square patch of light.

The driver greeted me and told me he didn't speak English. He was a tall wiry man with fierce black eyes. He was friendly and insisted I sit in the back as if I were precious cargo. As we joined the line of morning traffic out of the city, I had to lean forward if I wanted to see what was coming. The road skirted a hillside and we began to ascend into a dense fog. Snaking along the high valley pass, the cars and trucks ahead of us disappeared one by one until it was our turn and we were engulfed. I looked out at the whiteness. Cars heading back into Cluj passed by our windows like apparitions in a dream. I began to wonder where it was I was being taken. We seemed to be passing into a world beyond this one where we could see nothing but our own thoughts taking shape ahead of us on a blank white sheet.

I watched the back of the driver's head. He did not slow down. He did not crane forward to see into the mist. He simply continued as if nothing were happening. Close to the road I made out the shapes of short black trees, and here and there people were standing, like survivors of the apocalypse, hoping for a ride out of the gloom. I was reminded of the faces I see when I close my eyes and try to sleep. I leaned back. It seemed only fitting that I should be following the journey

made by a dead filmmaker into the mist. While in London searching for evidence relating to the shooting in Buffalo, I collected material relating to other shootings that had, in my mind, some bearing on events. On any number of occasions, I found myself in the National Gallery looking at Manet's re-assembled portrait of Ferdinand Maximilian at the moment he was executed by the Mexican army on the 19th June 1867.

Manet made three paintings and a lithograph of Emperor Maximilian's execution by Republican troops in Mexico, none of which were made public in Manet's lifetime. The middle painting is held in the National Gallery. At some point the picture was torn into pieces in order to create several works, before it was reassembled by Howard Hodgkin in 1979 into an arrangement based on Degas' earlier salvaging of the various fragments, which, like disassembled details blown apart in a storm, had been cut from the original and sent in different directions largely to alleviate the financial pressures of different owners at different times. The painting is very different from the one I recalled so often during those days and weeks: made up of the clean spats of the soldiers, the bare-headed and elegantly moustachioed Miramon, the grey brick wall and the clear blue mountains, it is in fact an imaginary compilation of several images, fragments seen in a mist. And yet the fragmentation appears symptomatic not so much of the subject matter but of the way in which the story was pieced together by Manet himself from a range of sources including drawings, newspaper reports and scattered photographs claiming to document the killing of the French  Emperor in Mexico. It was as if the precarious set of conditions – a failed invasion of a foreign land, an abandoned archduke, a rampant Mexican army – that determined the reception of the shooting in France had come, however unintentionally, to haunt Manet's picture, a foreign escapade that itself seemed to be beyond any final account. The execution of Maximilian in Mexico was a controversial and embarrassing event for the Napoleonic regime. It was also an international event. As one writer put it: *An extraordinary variety of prints and photographs of Maximilian circulated in Europe and America in the months after the execution.* Even in France, where the Imperial censors could supress unfavourable references to recent events, Manet would have had access to many images as well as to reports from Mexico that appeared in the press. I often wondered whether it was just that the information was incomplete or whether every experience, especially one so traumatic, must exist in this kind of close-range distance, within this fog of fragmentation.

As the mist thickened driving out of Cluj, I thought again of the smoke from the soldier's rifles merging with the clouds over the hills in Manet's painting. Some likened the gun smoke to the magnesium camera flashes of early photography, both machines, camera and gun – stopping time. Among my notes was a photograph, copied again and again almost to the point of non-existence, of Chris Burden being shot at point blank range by his friend, Bruce Dunlap, at 7pm on Tuesday 3ʳᵈ May 1971. The bullet went through Burden's left arm. It's not clear if the young American knew the painting by Manet but the grey reproduction of the instant he was shot with a .22 rifle offered up a peculiar tracing of the painting made a hundred years earlier – although on this occasion Dunlap's pose is a clear imitation of an otherwise invisible cameraman taking his shot. While trying to remember who it was I must have been before that time of great loss, it seemed that in the years since that evening in 1971, the young man in the photograph had begun a vague existence, in which he would, from that moment on, become a person taking place outside of himself. It was as if, through that violent and self destructive event, and most importantly of all, through its recording, he would move out of the life world common to us all and into that vast death world of the photograph and the film. Displaced across different times and spaces in the same way as the dead, he survives the gunshot but when he looks back at the images shot by the camera what will he see? He will not see himself. Instead he sees a ghost, or should I say he sees himself in the same way as I see him, as an outsider looking in on another person's life, wondering if it is at all possible to locate oneself or the things that happen to oneself in the evidence that remains? Could it be, instead, that these reports would take the place of who he had been and that life afterwards could only be measured against the loss embedded in these strange pictures, which, out of whatever sense of joy or despair, whether out of an attempt to remember or to improve how we forget, we labour to surround ourselves with.

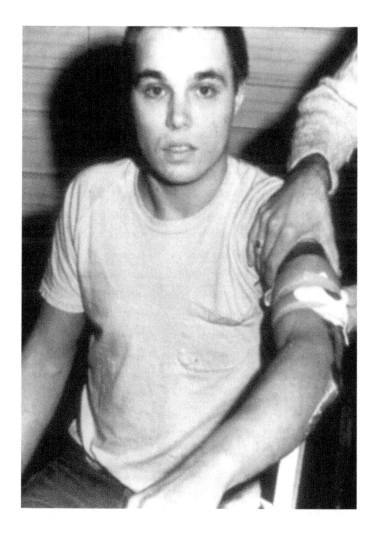

We suddenly dropped out of the fog and returned, as it were, to a world beneath the volcano permitted to exist for one more day. The sun shone down on a vast colour copy of the countryside and we were soon moving through the same lighted fields I had seen in the film by Sharits. I settled into the monotony of the new highway that ran in a straight line toward Bucharest, cutting the endless cornfields in two. I wondered if I could ever be a part of what I observed. Soon every inch of the world would be photographed, a word becoming more and more meaningless as a consequence.

In 1874, Eadweard James Muybridge stood trial for shooting and murdering his wife's lover, the theatre critic and former major in the British army, Harry Larkyns. In a hasty trial, Muybridge, who admitted to the murder and whose hair and beard during his four months in custody turned snowy white, was acquitted on grounds of diminished responsibility. Almost as soon as the trial ended, Muybridge fled the US to conduct a yearlong photographic survey of Central America sailing from San Francisco to Mexico, Panama and Guatemala in order to record coffee plantations and archaeologically significant sites in and around the major cities and ports.

Eadweard Muybridge, formerly Edward James Muggeridge of Kingston Upon Thames, turned to what he thought of as the art of photography by way of what I can only describe as a pre-modern precursor to the car accident. Some time around 1860, Muybridge, still a prospector of sorts pursuing various trades in the new world of the far western states of North America, was forced to return to England to recover from a stagecoach accident that left him

with serious head injuries. While he was there, according to
Hollis Frampton, he learnt the cumbersome, delicate craft of
the collodian wet plate, and discovered his vocation as a
photographer. He travelled back to California and in the
years that Manet was painting Maximillian's execution in
Paris, re-invented himself as the world's most famous
landscape photographer systematically photographing the
Far West and producing some two thousand images
reproduced and distributed in serial catalogues by Bradley &
Rulofson, the gallerists of Sacramento Street in San Francisco.
The extent of his restless journeying can be traced through
views of San Francisco, lighthouses of the Pacific Coast,
Vancouver Island, Alaska (as Director of Photographic
Surveys for the United States Government), Farallone Island,
the Pacific Railroad, Geyser Springs, Woodward's Gardens,
Yosemite, and Mariposa Grove. In contrast to his animal
locomotion studies that were shot in front of a false
background onto which was drawn a numbered grid, as if
from within a life-size mathematic experiment annihilating
any possible feeling of place, the landscapes create the
impression of a fabulous itinerary of quite impossible
geographical scope. I couldn't help but savour the vertigo of
each precipice and marvel at the spectral waterfalls. What I
am looking at, of course, is not water, not even the image of
water, but the virtual volume it occupies during the whole
time-interval of the exposure and this entire volume is both
so insignificant and so enormous as to make me feel quite
sick. Perhaps it is the impression induced by the catalogue, of
turning and examining page after page, but this is not the
overlapping of one landscape with another – the overlapping

of the imaginary and the observed, of so many images and their true place within a series – but what appears to be instead a form of no-man's land of memory and dream to which no one can return because its only reality is the photograph.

The pictures Muybridge made in Central America in the year after he shot and killed Harry Larkyns and less than a decade after the execution of Emperor Maximilian, stand out from his vertiginous body of work, I think, because of the strangely melancholic atmosphere of the images amassed against lost time, that do not record places so much as they document *time's ruination and its embodiment in architectural and corporeal detritus.* For many years I have carried with me a photocopy of an image that can be found in Muybridge's album entitled *The Pacific Coast of Central America and Mexico,* which shows what was even then

Guatemala's sprawling city of Antigua, the white buildings of the main church and plaza contrasting with the gloomy bulk of the black volcano that seems to loom forebodingly over the citizens below. I continued to hold onto the image even after I discovered, as I should have known all along, that the original print had been doctored by Muybridge so that the volcano in the image was not the volcano at Antigua but one imported from another photograph taken in another place. Looking back along the Romanian road on that late summer's day as we travelled at some speed away from Cluj, I thought once more of Muybridge's capacity to shift mountains and I wondered which copy of the world I was moving through now.

Some years ago, before events would get the better of me, I walked from my then home in Acton through the open spaces of Gunnersbury and on under the Great West Road, down to the wide river valley at Kew, with the intention of covering the few miles to Kingston upon Thames where Stephen Barber, who had been an acquaintance of mine since my studies as a graduate student and who knew something about these matters, held an office at the university. With the gardens to my left and the boat yards to my right, one or two of which were still in operation around the basin at London Lock where the River Brent empties into the Thames, I continued south, following the river as it snakes through Isleworth, Richmond, Ham and Twickenham then west past Strawberry Vale close to where Alexander Pope had a house. It was a warm midsummer's day, and in need of refreshment,

I climbed Richmond Hill to the Roebuck Inn. Taking my drink onto the road I gazed out over the flood-plains down to the widening Thames bending in the haze like a great jungle tributary away to the south and the west where the sun would eventually set even if that noon nothing seemed further from what was possible. I had read this was Turner's favourite view of the Thames and he often sought it out when living in Brentford with his uncle as a teenager in 1785 in the house where he would make his earliest known works.

By the time I was making my way through the leafy streets of Surbiton it was far later than I had intended. I nevertheless found Stephen, whose writings I admired for their out of the way quality and because they are nothing like the way he seemed to me at the time, in his office which was airless and dim despite the still relentless sunshine I knew existed somewhere beyond the poorly ventilated rooms of the university. The place was otherwise deserted for the holidays, adding to the office's impression of a hermit cell. There were few papers or books or other signs of life except for a large black briefcase standing open on the floor.

Stephen had recently returned from Los Angeles where he had been photographing derelict movie theatres. I leafed through the pictures he handed me showing the facades and interiors of the Roxy, the Rialto, the Palace and the Globe, each one empty and abandoned, scattered as it were along Stephen's sad spectrum of disrepair. After a while he confessed that he was most excited about showing me something else. He went to the bag and produced two large bundles of what looked like over-sized medical notes. They turned out to be a facsimile of Edward Muybridge's personal scrapbook that Stephen had just collected from the Muybridge archive at the Kingston Museum after many months of protracted negotiations. He had longed to study the scrapbook of the most famous Kingstonian since taking up his post at the university and now finally he could scrutinise the pages in detail and away from the attentions of the archive staff. Perhaps it was the heat or my fatigue from the river walk, but I could not help but question Stephen's excitement and in a regretfully sardonic tone I shrugged and said I was sure the scrapbook would once and for all reveal the man behind the mystery. Stephen looked past me and was quiet for a time.

Then he said, it was true, at first he had hoped naively that the scrapbook would tell us who the real Muybridge might have been. But he quickly let go of this delusion and as his studies of the scrapbook, which was made up of newspaper clippings, press releases, hand written notes, not to mention the many versions of his photographs reproduced in the press all carefully arranged across the 250 or so large format pages, progressed, Stephen could only marvel at something that appeared to be far more interesting: even in this most private of texts, Muybridge had gone to such incredible lengths to hide himself within the very fragments pieced together, as he must have known, precisely in order to reveal who the real Muybridge might have been, even if only to himself. Despite the amassed layers of material relating to the life and work of Eadweard Muybridge, the book is defined in the end by what it excludes. For instance, Stephen pointed out, as well as jettisoning all traces of many of his abandoned projects, it notably excludes the act of murdering with a pistol his wife's lover and the subsequent and very public trial.

Unsure how to return home, I visited the Museum at Kingston as it was closing for the day. Hurried by the staff and beyond any great feat of concentration, I managed to spend some time staring at one of the plates from Muybridge's Zoopraxiscope shows of the 1880s. The disc, which is quite large, almost half a metre in diameter, lay at the base of a display cabinet and showed the skeleton of a horse on eleven glass slides running along the black edge of the wheel-like plate. Lying there like that, the disc reminded me of the floor-plans or blueprints of Bentham's prisons with their corridors of cells leading into a central chamber. I don't know why I couldn't immediately move away from the cabinet. Perhaps it was because of the way the skeletons had been elongated in order to compensate for the distortions of time and space that would shorten and compress the poor beasts upon projection as if their bodies had been designed precisely in order to exist across a set of dimensions other than the one in which I was standing.

A tall man with long hair tied tightly at the back of his head apologised but the opening hours had passed. By way of consolation he offered to show me around the archives at a later date and wrote the number I should call on the back of a postcard. On leaving I took one final look at how the white skeletons, making their way interminably around the central opening, seemed to glow against the black background, ripped as they were from any particular time or context in some strange dance of the dead; awaiting reanimation at the hands of our absurd technologies of motion and light whereupon the eleven skeletons would become a single mystical ghost horse trapped in some looping and mobile parody of the eternal.

I didn't look at the postcard until it was growing quite dark and I was safely housed on the top deck of the bus that would take me back to Ealing Common. On the front of the postcard was an image that pulled me up short. It showed Bird in Flight, a photograph made in 1887 by Muybridge's great collaborator, friend, and champion of the new science of chronophotography, Etiennes-Jules Marey. Muybridge had pasted into his scrapbook a newspaper picture of either Marey or one of his bowler-hatted assistants in the pose of a

duck hunter or an officer of the artillery aiming his famed invention, the photographic gun, squarely at the sky. The rapid fire experiments of Etienne Joules Marey most embody the long association of the camera and the gun, which has always existed I think, not least because of media images of the dead, which circulate as forms of evidence or proof (like the photograph Manet owned of the shirt Maximilian wore on the day of his execution), and ever since the invention of the camera flash literally fired into the faces of its subjects causing a great cloud of smoke to plume in the air above the photographer draped under a black sheet. The association would continue into the new century with reports that the combustible and unstable materials of the new cinematic medium including the nitrate film stock through which these shadows were made would frequently catch fire upon projection, destroying

whole auditoria and engulfing those who had gone there to escape the world outside. Bird in Flight was one of the first photographs made with the photographic gun. In the image a single animal has been transfigured into multiple versions of itself captured at various stages along the translucent stream of its flight through a space of complete blackness devoid of any reference to a place or time. I had seen the image before but on this occasion, suspended in the artificial glare of the bus passing through the west London night, I could only stare at the remainder of the gull escaping out of the frame as if into some other freedom, those luminescent past versions of the same bird that even in its multiplied appearance is of course long gone.

In 1923 Brancusi made the first version of a sculpture he would repeat in different materials throughout his life, instinctively embracing the photographic impulse toward infinite reproduction. He called the work L'Oiseau dans 'espace, Bird in Space. Thinner at its base than its tip, the slender upright form always reminds me of a television screen seen side-on, a slit of light in an otherwise dark and empty room. Some described Bird in Space as an attempt to remember, as if through work a lost world could be restored. Others described it as Brancusi tracing the arc of an idea across the night sky of his mind. Most shapes moulded by other people bear some correspondence with those found in nature, or those human inventions that originate in an endless quest for order, stability and permanence. The circle of the moon, for instance, or the quadrilateral of the grave repeated in pursuit of the perfect version, the ideal dimensions that will

express without words something eternal and pure. It is possible to find the purest expression of these elemental forms in the construction of church buildings or homes for the insane. In Buffalo, where Paul Sharits was shot, the ward corridors of the state asylum designed by Henry Hobson Richardson were 210 feet long and 15 feet wide with 16 foot ceilings, according to specifications developed by Dr. Thomas Kirkbride, who believed coherent and predictable environments were calming and restorative. On occasion an artist, like a scientist discovering new codes of DNA or new genetic modulations, comes upon a shape nobody has encountered before. But for a long time Brancusi's bird was the shape of all the birds I had murdered as a boy, the same birds that in the weeks before I left England would not let me sleep.

Nobody can know how many times Brancusi re-cast Bird in Space but the endless task connects in my mind with the house Sarah Winchester built during the first two decades of the Twentieth Century. Sarah Pardee was born in New Haven, Connecticut in 1840; at eighteen she married William Wirt Winchester, whose father manufactured the repeating rifle, that great instrument of repetition, reproduction and death, that helped "Win the West." Obsessed by the loss of an infant daughter and by the immature death of her husband a few years later, she concluded that the ghosts of victims of the rifle, Indians in particular, were out to get her. Her fears were confirmed by a medium in Boston, who told her she would be safe only if she undertook to build a house on which work would continue eternally, night and day, in which case she would expect to live forever.

Such a project was not beyond her means in 1882, when she disposed a fortune of $20 million and a tax-free income of $1,000 a day. Accordingly, she transplanted herself from Connecticut to the Santa Clara Valley (it is not known why she chose this particular location) and began remodelling an existing eight room farm house in a project that would last until her death, in 1922, finally stilled the continuous noise of the hammers. When I first saw the film documenting the journey Paul Sharits made to Târgu Jiu in a basement beneath the sculpture studios at St Martin's School of Art (a room as dark as Kafka's burrow) the soundtrack was continuously interrupted by the noise of hammering and god knows what else. To this day, I think of the main staircase in the now abandoned Charing Cross Road campus, where a panel in one of the windows looking out over the network of rearward fire escapes that seemed to fly quite freely through the air only to connect one invisible exit with another, had been removed and replaced with a mirror, creating the odd impression that part of the interior was floating in the world beyond in the now foreshortened middle-distance; and that the outside world was in fact a strange construction of the world within. The mirror had been installed by David Dye when he was studying sculpture at St Martin's in the late 1960s, and, either because nobody had noticed or because it was assumed to be a quirk of the original 1930s architecture, the mirror was left well alone until the building was sold to property developers in 2010 and the college moved north to its current home behind the train terminals at Kings Cross and Saint Pancras. I haven't been inside the building since – where the original set of doors, that still carry the embossed lintels designed and cut by Eric Gill, is now a private entrance to exclusive loft apartments, once the painting studios lit by vast skylights that spanned the ceilings of the building's top floor – but I like to think the mirror has continued to go unnoticed and thus undisturbed except by those who happen to catch sight of themselves floating in mid-air, as it were, startled by their presence in two places at once.

While making my way along the stairwells and corridors of the old college, in which the sounds of largely unidentifiable activities reverberated through the walls, I often thought of Sarah Winchester's mansion in California and the torment of the ghosts of those murdered by her father in-law's invention; that world of continuous earthly construction keeping the spirit world of death and memory at bay. I think this association had much to do with David's mirror and with his film, Western Reversal, made originally in 1973 and which he showed me a few years before he died suddenly of a stroke in the first weeks of 2015. In Western

Reversal, which is more of a sculpture than a film, David projected a super 8 copy of a budget 1940s cowboy movie, Flaming Arrows, onto a bank of small square mirrors that could each be angled in 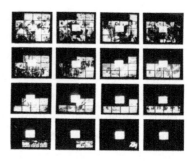 different directions at once. When he flicked on the projector the film bounced onto the mirrors and, split into sixteen different pieces, the film was sprayed around the dark auditorium. Watching the fractured film, no easy feat as parts of it were taking place behind me while others were scattered about the ceiling above my head, and attempting to connect horses and men running and shooting rifles in directions that now ceased to connect, I wasn't sure if the gaps between the fragments were what I was seeing or if these gaps were in fact the secret spaces that live in all images, into which we enter and abandon part of ourselves, only for these fragments to return at other times as something unfamiliar and strange. I remember a tree being felled, a stagecoach overturned and set on fire to create a smokescreen, a Gatling Gun and smoke signals made by cowboys and not the blacked up actors posing as *Injuns* too busy butchering unarmed white men already wounded and lying on the ground. Because of the mirror fragmentation, figures moving through disjointed hillsides collided at once with desert spaces and then with woodland or a river scene. I also remember that the Indians in Flaming Arrows were modernised by the rifles they carried making them doubly terrifying no doubt for audiences of the time. This was no primitive foe; these tribesmen could aim, shoot and reload as well as any white man. No doubt this disjointed shootout, as David trained each of the mirrors onto a single spot at the centre of the actual screen, went on for all but a matter of minutes but it seemed to me that the entire history conflating in my mind, the camera and the gun, was being played out across the walls and ceiling of the old cinema which appeared suddenly to be the encapsulation of an entire century of perception and thought rather than an everyday movie auditorium. Of course, looking back, I'm not sure that I ever saw Western Reversal in a cinema; more likely the projector would have been installed for the evening or an afternoon in a makeshift screening space otherwise used as a classroom or a lecture hall. Many of the rooms in the old St Martin's buildings had no fixed use. What was for one term a storeroom would the next be an office or a darkroom for developing film. And of course, all of those rooms are now gone, lost to our continuous urge for destruction and the seemingly perpetual desire to replace one artificial world with the next.

I had been told the journey to Târgu Jiu would take several hours and that the roads through the mountains were not in good repair. Once we had descended into the farmlands south of Turda we made good time along the highway that linked the cities of the northern provinces. Soon, however, we turned off and headed west toward the Jiu Valley. After three hours the road narrowed and we were forced to make several detours before coming to a roadblock; no vehicles were permitted into the final pass through the valley. It wasn't clear why the road was closed or when it would reopen. A few desolate looking cars were parked across the junction. My driver stopped and got out. He couldn't tell me anything even if he wanted to. I opened the door and crossed the road to a dilapidated cantina. Huge logging trucks had pulled up in front of the building raised out of the mud. None of the drivers of the trucks were around. I climbed the steps to a creaking terrace: the screen door was locked and the place reeked of abandonment, but a man and a boy were playing cards in the shade. I asked, as best I could, if there was a toilet. The man's face did not change but the boy jumped up. He nodded and smiled pointing to a shack behind the bar. As I moved out across the yard I felt like an unarmed man in a war who would never make it home. The toilet smelled terribly. I used the small urinal jammed roughly into a corner as quickly as I could, and my piss ran out of the door between my feet. Looking down I saw that nothing had been plumbed in. Feeling sick that I had only made things worse I walked back across the terrace, the boy jumping up once more, waving me goodbye, the man staring at the floor. I found my driver, one foot up on the wheel arch, bent over a road atlas that was falling apart. After a while he lit another cigarette, and made several phone calls. I assumed we would have to abandon our journey when suddenly he stubbed out his cigarette and said, *Okay. We go.*

We retraced our route back through the town that had grown up around the quarries and power stations before turning off onto a road that led through a set of encampments and rough farmland. We passed horse drawn-carts. An occasional motor vehicle had been left to rust along the route. My driver stopped briefly to question a man standing at the side of the road with a plastic bag. The man pointed; I leaned forward. Ahead of us I could see forested hills rising up into the distance and beyond that the peaks of a jagged mountain range, and as we continued the road climbed steeply and we were soon crawling along a forest track. The road zigzagged for several miles and with every mile the road worsened. Huge potholes forced the car to swing toward the edge of the track and I looked down through trees that barely concealed the sheer drop. Occasionally a stream cut across the track and my driver had to gun the car hoping the water was no deeper than it looked. The only signs of life were the paper and plastic bottles littering the side of the track. I sat motionless in my seat and realised I had been holding my breath. As my driver swung the car around yet another hairpin bend the road levelled out onto a ridge high above the treeline. Miraculously we arrived at a junction with a brand new road winding luxuriously into the distance – and suddenly we could travel unhindered over the Carpathian landscape. It seemed as if we had reached a magical land closer to the sky than the earth, the sweeping hills reminding me of shadow lands, an endless rolling landscape made up of mountains and moorland that would continue on and on until it reached some glimmering sea.

We pulled into a layby and my driver got out. He stretched and smiled, motioning that he needed a break. I watched him walk off into the distance and I thought we had come to the end of the world. But miraculously he returned and I realised I had not asked him his name. Neither had he inquired after

mine. Back on our way something had changed. For several miles all I could do was to gaze at the back of his head. I felt a sudden need to tell him everything. But I sat in silence and looked at the hills below.

Sometime in the 1920s, Brancusi bought a camera from his American friend Man Ray. He often pointed at the camera, like a magical emblem, and told those who would listen it was impossible to see the world in the way he once did. Rather than the Pascalian figure found in typical accounts of the visionary artist, sealed off by the high walls of his studio from the social and political upheavals of the time, Brancusi frequently wandered the streets of Paris and made long summer journeys into the countryside beyond the city. Wherever he went he carried his camera. He had a particular eye for ruined buildings as well as animals and birds. He photographed children playing in the dusty streets around his

Impasse Ronsin studio. As well as many photographs, Brancusi left behind several fragments of film. One of these fragments recorded part of the train journey Brancusi made on his return to the Jiu Valley while construction of his sculpture garden was underway. It seems odd to think of this journey as going back; he was not ten years old when he ran away from the hills around Târgu Jiu. I have only seen stills of the film he made on that train ride. Showing the view from the locomotive the silvery bands of the river, reflecting nothing, cut the images into black and white lines. Laid out in strips, these stills remind me of the writing books I used at school, I remember marking out the lines on every page with a pencil and ruler for what seemed like hours and the strange sensation of turning back to the beginning where I would write my name.

By 1937, when he was commissioned to build his ensemble at Targu-Jiu, Brancusi would have been in his early 60s and at the zenith of his career. His sculptures were coveted all around the world. Before any of his sculptures left the studio bound for museums in America and cities across Europe he painstakingly photographed each one. While in Cluj, I had made arrangements to view a private collection of some of these photographs held in the library on Corvin Matin. I waited in the small reading room as a nervous librarian, watching me with some suspicion, brought two large boxes bound tightly with white cord. *No cameras*, she said; *no copies*.

These were nearly all pictures taken by Brancusi himself. On the back of each image a hand written note gave the title of the work and the location of its new home: Philadelphia,

Chicago, New York, Buffalo. I wondered if it was through one of these objects exiled to America that Paul Sharits had first come as it were into contact with Brancusi. Like most people

I had only seen Brancusi's work in books. The pictures had a power of their own and were just as carefully constructed. And yet I wondered what it was Brancusi was attempting to hold onto, what this amassing of evidence would prove. *We photograph things*, Kafka once wrote, *in order to drive them out of our minds.*

In one of the photographs of Princess X, an object that was at one time banned from public display in Paris, the perfectly smooth surface, like a convex mirror, arrests forever a single moment of attention. Later, I would have a copy of the same image I found in a book blown up expecting to see Brancusi behind his camera reflected in the smooth outer shell along with other details of the otherwise invisible room, but he was nowhere to be seen. He must have gone to great lengths, it seemed to me, to conceal himself. In my notes I had recorded the observations of one of Brancusi's greatest critics: *the work of Brancusi is style-less*, he writes. *The sculptures often need each other but they do not need the sculptor or his personality. The effacement of self is known to art as the classical sign of the artist. In Brancusi's case it is his sculpture. He often dwelt on the thought that there is a purpose in all things. To get to it one must go beyond oneself.* For some reason, in my notes, I had crossed out the final line and replaced it with: One must destroy oneself. Looking through the pictures Brancusi had left behind, it seemed clear to me that the photographic copy was never anything but an obliteration of reality, so that what is real has come to rely on photography and film, not the other way round. At one point, however, I had to pause. For a long time I gazed at a picture of a marble from 1914: New born, or Head of a Sleeping Child. Things that were far away seemed suddenly near and the room I was in began to recede into a terrible distance. But I was calm. There were, I knew, other photographs in another box that I could never bring myself to examine.

At last we had arrived at Târgu Jiu, which appeared, delightfully, to be a city of gardens. Wide and neatly ordered streets somehow suggested the countryside was never far away. None of the houses seemed to be more than one or two stories and each sat within a square of lawn clearly delineated by wire fencing laden with beans and tomato plants. My journey felt careless, suddenly, reckless even, as if I had been pursuing enigmas through empty space. I thought of the great migrations of the world: if people did not journey, the world would never change. It seemed as if it was only in recent times that people had taken to living in houses and conducting their lives within circumscribed locations.

My driver dropped me at the entrance to a park. A scattering of trees and shrubs lined the perimeter but it was an otherwise open space, and those who walked in it were never far from the main road through Târgu Jiu. I walked across the field burnt dry in places by the late summer sun toward the Infinite Column; I thought of Paul Sharits making his own way across the same park, trying to learn through his camera something of the spaces between Brancusi's stone and metal works and the strange city where they still stood. I preferred the name in its original French: Column sans fin or column without end. From a safe distance it seemed to rise into the sky in dulled but glinting copper pieces and was anything but infinite. Most cities now contained buildings that were taller – housing blocks, office towers, cooling stacks – none of which made any claim on the infinite. On completion in 1937 local priests gathered to bless the infinite Column, their benediction confirming the hope it would indeed hold up the sky.

Brancusi's idea, of course, was that the column would continue in the mind, that any pattern, if it were based on a series of repeating forms, had the potential to continue endlessly in the imaginations of those looking at it, and this was something Sharits had clearly understood. As with anything, the object changes as you approach. For a long time I circled the column half thinking it might be possible to make it disappear, that I was there entirely by mistake, that it was not some strange conductor or lightning rod of my emotions. I sat beneath a tree and wondered what I should do. We had arrived not long past noon and the sky was unbearably blue; I was hot and thirsty and concerned that this was all a terrible mistake. For a long time I stared up into the branches of the tree. When I looked back a wedding party had gathered. The new bride wore a red dress and from where I was sitting I could tell she was happy. She and her husband, clad in a white suit so clean it gleamed spotlessly in the sun, posed for a photographer with the column flying up into the cloudless sky behind them. I wasn't sure what it might signify or what they were hoping for. Virility maybe or for the day to never end? For children? Many of them? I watched the rest of the group move about in directions that looked from my vantage point to  be preordained. One person crossed toward the bride while another moved away and so on like bees in a hive. They seemed to be subject to certain rhythms set in motion in accordance with a pattern agreed on at another time, and along which lines they permitted one another to occupy space. I wondered if I had fallen asleep and if this was nothing but a construction of my mind, a drama staged for no one but myself. When I looked up the party was gone.

In a quiet corner of the park I came upon a run-down tourist centre. Despite its uninviting exterior the interior was bright and neatly arranged. There were postcards for sale as well as mugs, bags and pens. A woman sat alone behind a counter and nodded as I walked in. Her expression did not change and for a moment I thought she was expecting me. I began to say something but stopped. She smiled and continued to write numbers into a thick ledger on her desk. I picked up a whiskey glass bearing a black and white portrait of Brancusi and put it down again. In one corner I noticed a wooden dining chair and considered sitting down, but instead, I crossed into a vestibule, which was empty except for a handful of framed photographs hanging above an ancient gas heater. The photographs showed the Infinite Column during its construction. For a long time I studied these before and after images. As with every magic trick we need to know how it was done. In one of the pictures a black zigzag had been drawn onto the site where the column without end would eventually stand. In July 1937, there was no suburban park, nothing but a dirt track led up to the site of the unmade work sketched onto the grey sky like a future world written into existence. Or was this the end of something?

The gap between fact and fiction seemed so literal, suddenly, like a game played by children and I had to force myself to take my eyes off the hand-drawn likeness of what was now reality and think carefully about my arms and legs as I walked back across the room. I wondered if every moment in time contained some ghostly drawing, referencing neither a future nor a past but a faded imprint of what might have been, hanging in space like a picture in a room or an ultrasound sending messages back from what had been lost forever.

I took a deep breath and searched for somewhere to sit. I had become accustomed to my eyes playing tricks on me. In the weeks before I left for Cluj, I spent many evenings in the backroom where I write rearranging images into groups based on quite arbitrary systems of what seemed to me interrelating themes. These groups tended to shift and morph under my fingers until, exhausted by the task and over-whelmed by the amassing imagery, I would fall back in my chair unable to remember how I had begun or in what form any of these images could possibly connect. On one such evening, fatigued once more to the point of despair, I found two slides I had had made for a lecture some years before in a file marked *execution and memory*. Out of sheer frustration, and without even considering the content of the transparencies, I loaded the slides into the revolving magazine of a slide projector, flicked on the bulb and adjusted the lens until the first image resolved into the large impression of a pinewood clearing. I flicked to the next image in the carousel, which looked to be its double except the sunlit clearing was less defined and the middle of the frame was occupied by a tall male figure dressed in black. I flicked back to the first image, which was clearly not intended to be first, and there was the same figure lying supine on the ground. The two pictures were made by Bas Jan Ader and I must have had the slides produced in order to see the work in the form originally exhibited by Ader in 1972 in a small space in Holland that I have never visited. The images have been reproduced side-by-side in magazines and books but I wanted to see them projected, only then could I see that the two images combined to produce a form of movement, one I felt to be taking place, but that this movement was somehow suspended or transmitted from another state, which had to remain invisible. The images are inevitably read from left to right as with all before and after shots. The left-hand image contained the standing Ader surrounded by the vast pines. The second image, the one I had returned to first on that bleak winter's evening, shows Ader lying horizontally, a black line or dash, along the ground like a visual echo of the trees that had been felled.

Looking back at my papers from the time, I found that I must have already corrected the order of events in Ader's slides – the implied film sequence – perhaps in anticipation of these notes. There is little that is natural about a tree being felled to satisfy human purposes even if, as one observer suggests, Ader *iterates features found in nature* and that the tree pictures are a *type of homology*.

Ader was born in rural Holland in 1942. During World War Two his father, Bastiaan, who was a minister with the Dutch Reform Church, was a major organiser in the resistance movement, helping Jews who worked in an Amsterdam hospital find safe shelter in the countryside. This already dangerous task was made all the more difficult by the geographical position of the Ader home, located in Nieuw-Beerta, a tiny hamlet close to the Dutch-German border. Shuttling Jews in and out had to be done under cover of darkness or the shroud of fog, with local members of the resistance relying upon their knowledge of footpaths to traverse the muddy fields. Bastiaan Ader would have had to make himself and his cargo invisible, melting into the landscape by pursuing the contours of the land as if they were not of the ground beneath them but part of the very substance of who they were. Of course, it didn't end well. Ader's mother, Johanna Adriana Ader-Appels, was frequently harassed by German soldiers and eventually forced to leave the home in Nieuw-Beerta while Bastiaan Ader was arrested during the final months of the war. The young Ader had memories of artillery fire and the flashes of distant combat seen from the second-story windows of his family home. On at least one occasion, German soldiers ransacked their home, telling Ader's mother to pack her things and remove herself and her two young children. Clothes were scattered about violently, pictures, furniture and personal effects thrown carelessly out of the windows, an image that would become a recurring theme in Ader's work. Worse, Ader's father, then in central Holland, was arrested for his involvement with the resistance and imprisoned by the Germans. On the night of November 20th, 1944, just sixteen days after his second child, Erik, was born he and six other prisoners were pulled from their cells and taken to a spot in the woods where they were to face a firing squad. Ader's father asked to go last in order to comfort the others and prepare them for their journey to the next world. This generous act meant that he had to see each of his companions killed. He then met his fate with a strength of conviction that haunted his son for the rest his life.

Someone once said to me, Bas Jan Ader later wrote: *I can well imagine that you are so obsessed with the fall; it's because your father was shot. But that is obviously a far too anecdotal interpretation*, he said. *Everything is tragic because people always lose control of processes, of matter, of their feelings. That is a much more universal tragedy and that cannot be visualised from an anecdote.* And anyway, what could it mean to re-enact such a thing? What would one base it on? Bas Jan Ader was not there. He only knew the stories he was told as a boy growing up in the countryside. Like a film actor imitating some previous role once seen in a film

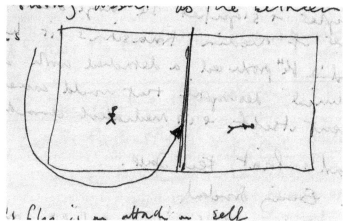

that has long since been destroyed, with only the remembered impressions of a few fleeting scenes to go on, he must have seen some connection between the two finally futile activities: attempting on the one hand to copy nature and on the other to re-enact the past. This is why, I think, I drew, in my notes, an arrow pointing to the vertical line that divides the two pictures. The vertical edge of the adjoining frames creates a hazy border that is and isn't there. Hovering just outside of resolution, this fuzzy boundary, I realised that evening in winter, is as much of a figure in the foreground as the young man dressed in black. I am not sure how Ader made the photographs, whether he was alone in the woods and the camera was fired by a timer or whether he was accompanied by someone else, there to shoot on his command. Either way, the axis that divides the two shots seems to hold this invisible presence in place, the camera and the executioner meeting, as it were, in the uncertain lamplight, or at least this is what I begin to think as I flicked the projectors off and made my way out of the house and into the dark streets outside.

Returning the following day, I found my key no longer worked in the lock and I had to go away.

When I rose from the wooden chair in the tourist office the woman behind the desk looked up, startled, as if seeing me for the first time. Then she smiled and asked where I was from. She had lived in Târgu Jiu all her life and had no intention of leaving. *Where would I go? What would I do?* She said. I didn't know what to say to this – that none of these things mattered? I told her I was passing through. She nodded and looked toward the door. Then she said: *If you keep going east long enough you will find yourself once more heading west*. On leaving I wondered how many of the tourists who arrived in her office – washed up on her beach as it were – had received this strange message.

Back in the park I walked across the grass. Once again I was lost. I looked at my watch. It seemed as if many hours had gone by since my arrival but only a few minutes had passed. I felt tiny under the enormous sky and had the odd impression I was watching myself from hundreds of feet above, a black speck moving over an empty field. I headed for the cover of the trees. Here the park had been abandoned. Broken bottles and the same strewn debris I had seen along the sides of the mountain roads had collected between untended foliage. I came to what looked like an unfinished platform cast in rough concrete half obscured by dry grass. This was the site of Brancusi's missing monument.

Looking around I felt as if I had trespassed onto the scene of some obscure crime. There is disagreement surrounding what exactly Brancusi intended for this edge of the park. Some claimed it would be a large table, others described a structure that resembled a bed. For whatever reason, nothing was built. And yet I couldn't help thinking something significant had been removed as if here was another monument, not to what was gone exactly but to what had never come to pass.

Keeping under the trees I cut back along the edge of the park toward the road that linked the recreation ground and the Column Sans Fin with the city gardens where the remainder of the ensemble could be found. As I did so I began to wonder how I had come to be in this place, I felt suddenly as if I had forgotten as much as I could remember. All points of departure seemed to be ghostly shadows – no more than a glance at a photograph or a picture in a book. As I left the park and crossed the street a large dog leapt against a fence. My train of thought broken, I had the distinct impression I had seen this dog before. I turned to see a boy and a girl giggling and pointing at the strange man startled by the hound. I often thought of the film Sharits made in Târgu Jiu as an extended flashback – an involuntary picture flashing up in front of one's eyes seemingly out of nowhere.

The film Sharits made in Târgu Jiu seemed to orbit a hidden trauma – some event that could not be described, except in terms of what had been forgotten, as if only through its forgetting could what happened be experienced at all. What distinguishes a traumatic event, I would soon learn, is its irreversibility. The clock cannot be turned back. The next time you wake there is the unavoidable fact: nothing will be as it was. This is the opposite of film, which since its conception has resisted temporal rules. Buildings raised to the ground can be miraculously restored; bombs can be thrown back into planes; animals and people can be raised from the dead. Reversing, replaying, rewinding the film, any scene of devastation can be returned to what it once had been. And yet this ghostly means of reconstructing a world we think we understand, forever on the verge of extinction, has its own vulnerability. Film wears down and fades or burns and breaks, like the people and places it renders in light and shadow. And so here I was, unsure if what I was seeing was real or if I was re-living the fragments of a film I could barely remember having seen.

While the mile-long road between the parks ran in a straight line, a church some called St Peters and others called St Paul positioned half way along the route obscured any view a walker might enjoy from one gate to the other. The few cars that passed me had to circle the building, which stood in the centre of an island – or so it seemed – detached from the city around it. There were no trees. Nothing offered any shade for the weary that travelled to its doors. A wooden bench, providing some comfort, was occupied by two men sitting upright, their eyes fixed on the heavy entrance. From the back as I approached they appeared much alike and I assumed they were brothers. When I passed I was shocked to see that one of the men was no more than a teenager while the other, his face deeply lined around sunken eyes and a toothless mouth, was an elderly man. For a brief moment, it struck me that the two men, who did not speak or appear to be aware of one another, were in fact the same person at either end of an unhappy life. For most people visiting the ensemble the walk between the two parks was an inconvenience at best, to be put out of mind once it had been endured, like moving between terminal buildings at an airport. Yet the walk stands out in my memory even if I cannot be sure in what order things took place. The men on the bench were a kind of half-way point waiting between one world and the next. But I am not certain of whether the face I saw at a window or the child who approached me on a bicycle or the young women who laughed as I went by were real; part of an ordered series of events.

When Sharits made his film about Brancusi's sculpture ensemble at Târgu Jiu, he wanted to challenge the common-held understanding that the sculptures existed independently of one another, as isolated objects ripped out of any particular time or place. He was more interested in the spaces between each monument than what they might mean on their own terms: an uncertain space of light and faces, of dust and animal sounds, constantly changing as the life of the city evolved. Only a stranger, it seemed to me then, could move through a world like this. Yet as I passed along Calea Eroiler, I could not shake the feeling I was looking at the street through glass, no matter how close these apparitions came. Rather than something continuous my path from one park to the other came to me then, and now, in the form of disunited fragments scattered about me. It seemed I was travelling along the edge of an ellipse, the horizon bending out of sight as one blind spot was replaced with another. Disconnected, at that moment, from everything that was real, I could only observe each sensation of my movement through space without being a part of it. Stopping to catch my breath I could hear a piano being played quite badly. Listening to the stuttering notes I was reminded of a child taking its first steps. Perhaps a nephew or a niece was learning their scales or perhaps the sound was the faltering work of someone who could never get anything right.

I crossed the street. Once again I had the impression I was watching myself from above, only now there was nowhere to hide. I have read descriptions of out of body experiences, where those caught between themselves and the impression they have of who they are, rise to the ceiling and look down on their bodies or drift into the form of an animal or a person looking back at a stranger through a fence or across a station platform. But this was different. According to my notes, Brancusi had an aerial view of the city in mind when he designed the ensemble. In the years following its completion warplanes would photograph every inch of Europe's cities from the sky before the same aircraft would dismember forever that world from its image. I wondered if Brancusi had somehow anticipated this united machine of war and photography and the distortions it would produce. The ensemble no longer resembled a series of connecting points, as the American filmmaker would have it, but an image of separation, of order and chaos, of a world blown apart, torn from the stories it tells of itself.

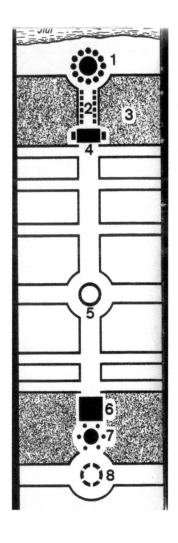

Perhaps in the end the plan made more sense from the sky. From the street I could not grasp what was happening. All I could do was to continue. At one point I crossed a railway line. There were no barriers or signals, the road simply carried on in a broken path across the rails. I looked up. Three large raptors circled in the warm air rising from the ground. Something must have died on the line, or so I told myself, as I made my way across the rails. Without warning a freight train rumbled through the crossing. I stopped and listened – it seemed to take an age for the locomotive to pass – but I did not turn around. Looking back, I now realise I was afraid there would be nothing there. No train. No movement. Only the buzzards spiralling in the sky above my head. In the early part of the Twentieth Century, it was often said that seeing a film was like being hit by a train, that the vehicles, animals and people animated on the screen were more real than life itself, chasing audiences from the darkness of the auditorium for fear they would be crushed by onrushing machines. Unsurprisingly, the first film that attempted to tell a story was a film about trains. Up until then, cinema had been an art of separation, the production of single moments, each one an island without a past. In those early films the present no longer became past; it was simply replaced by another version of what was happening, again and again. But in this new form of movie, order and sequence were not just the wiping away of what had come before, but an accumulation of sensory associations we now call narrative. Phantoms connected interiors that otherwise had nothing to do with one another. As the bandits in *The Great Train Robbery* escape into the woods, the signalman's daughter raises the alarm in a tavern. What was in reality a jumble of fragments, the hold up, the chase, the fire fight, good winning out in the end, those things we cling to, that meaning can be tied to events, were held together in the air suddenly by some invisible structure. That is, until the lead bandit, only recently killed, blown from his horse and left to rot on the ground, is alive and well and staring into our world. He lifts his pistol and fires.

Standing in that empty road, it struck me then that the shooting of Paul Sharits in 1982, described by a barman and a passer-by, both of whom missed the firing of the gun, was not in fact an all but forgotten moment in a man's life, but more likely a scene from an old western glimpsed accidently whilst flicking between television channels, a moment recalled quite by chance in another time and another place, one that haunts the violent obliterations inherent in everything we think we see.

It was then I realised I had lost the feeling in my hands and feet, and I wondered if I was moving at all or if in fact the world was drifting past me like a mechanical amusement triggered by a coin dropped into a box. When I came to my senses, I was standing at the side of a busy road among a crowd of people waiting for the lights to change. I crossed the street into the cool of the main city gardens, and stood for a long time in front of the Gate of the Kiss.

Suddenly calm, I looked back at the way I had come through the square window formed by the Gate of the Kiss. My recent walk felt like a distant memory and I was glad to have something to fix upon, as the sheer weight of Brancusi's monument rooted me to the spot. From where I stood, it should have been possible to see the Column Without End framed in the aperture of the crude arch. But again, the view is obscured by the dome of St Peter's. Instead, the opening captures the immediate environment like a badly taken photograph, cancelling out what I had seen only an hour or so before. For a time I was glad of this invitation to forget and watched as a group of tourists gathered to photograph the artwork and each other. Locals passed without giving the visitors a second glance. As far as the men playing chequers and chess under the nearby trees were concerned we were all strangers here. As the tourists moved away toward their next target in a buzz of muted excitement an elderly couple approached the Gate of the Kiss and posed for a photograph. The man and the woman stood in the gap between the two solid pillars, an image within an image, before they also moved away. And so the cycle continued, without end it seemed. This was, it seemed, a meeting place for all things that would in time be gone, an ode to patience that even the nearby beech and ash trees could not match.

I waited in the shade of the late afternoon. In my memory of the film by Paul Sharits, the camera trains across the edge of the stone so that the lens and the surface almost meet. I often wondered what this need to get as close as possible said about the condition Sharits was in. But of course the man behind the camera is hidden from view. I can only see what he was – or, more likely, what he wasn't – seeing: his mother's suicide, his divorce from his wife, the endless fights for money to make his films, his addictions to drugs and alcohol. Indeed, it seemed to me then, as it does now, that any attempt to see the world as closely as possible – in the fullness of its flesh – becomes a study in blindness. Instead, what I remember most about that section of film is his voice and the metallic sound of a microphone being tapped against the stone. On my own arrival in the city gardens, I could not get any closer to the Gate of the Kiss, and yet, for a time, I struggled to drag myself away. If I had studied the monument more closely I would have seen the great pock marks, like the evidence of past acne, burnt into the stone by time, a sure sign the Gate of the Kiss would return, inevitably, to the empty air it had attempted to throw a frame around forming a picture – not a picture of the world, like a photograph, but a picture taking place in the world, like a film, a picture which would also one day be gone.

The final part of the ensemble, a series of thirty knee-high, hourglass pedestals, ran in sections along an avenue of trees leading up to a clearing where the Table of Silence stands close to the bank of the river Jiu. While already late in the afternoon, the day was still warm and bright, and as I passed under the trees I realised that the light which seemed to tremble in the air all around me was just as it had been in the film that was shot so many years before and I wondered I if I had arrived somehow on the same day. I found myself counting off each pedestal as I walked, automatically, I thought, until I remembered Sharits had counted each pedestal as he passed by. I remembered thinking the rhythmic chanting contrasted with the frenetic editing as if he was attempting to unpick the mystery of what he had seen that day in Romania in 1978 – perhaps when he was a different person, one he no longer recognised in full. Nonetheless, I walked through the gardens with a lightness of foot, like a mountaineer in the final phase of an arduous climb once the ground has levelled out.

Unaware of my approach, a group of children played on the Table of Silence and I stood not far from where their mothers talked in the shade. I watched as three girls chased a boy round and round the white circular form as if they were orbiting a moon. The girls were older and seemed to know what they were doing. They all ran breathlessly until the boy stopped and turned. The girls also halted and for a moment everything was still. Then, laughing, they once again resumed the chase only this time in reverse, the boy, a head shorter, his socks about his ankles, on the heels of his sister and her friends. I wondered what they would do if they ever caught each other or was the whole point to keep making circles around things that didn't move? After a time the two mothers embraced and moved away, calling to their children. I watched as they separated into two groups of strikingly similar size and shape, one heading south and the other north along the river.

Suddenly alone it was with an almost overwhelming sense of relief that I took a seat on one of the twelve stools encircling Brancusi's stone table. The circular limestone slab felt quite out of proportion with everything around and, as I ran my hand over the weathered surface I smiled at a notice forbidding any human contact with the sculpture. Brancusi had knowingly employed calcareous rock which would, eventually, wear down to nothing despite the municipality's best efforts to arrest the effects of time. In the dusty ground about my feet I observed the still fresh footprints of the children who were now heading home. One perfectly formed shoeprint made the hairs on the back of my neck stand on end. It looked tiny from where I was sitting and I wondered if I was looking at the imprint through a telescope from upon some distant hill. I felt like Crusoe startled to discover he was not so alone on his island or Conrad's Almeyer wiping away his daughter's footprint, not so much to deny the pain of her betrayal but to wipe away the folly of his own beleaguered mind.

The president was right. I had come to the wrong place. I took out the page from the Hotel Sebastopol and laid it flat on the rough surface of Brancusi's Table. Staring at the handwritten marks I wondered how I could finish what I had started, whether it would be possible to jam things together or pull them apart and I was struck by the attempts we make, despite everything, to reach into the mist, into what we cannot see, to find some connection in the different lives and times that have continued somehow on the other side of these all encompassing screens displaying so much and keeping so much hidden. I knew it was hopeless. Nothing I could say or do would make up for what was gone.

I cannot be sure how long I sat at the Table of Silence. It could have been a matter of minutes or for all I know several hours might have passed. I was aware of various figures moving in and out of range, tourists, professionals on their way home from work, teenagers strolling hand in hand, so that I was rarely alone and the table was anything but silent. As the shadows lengthened I became conscious of a park attendant who was, I sensed, deciding whether or not I could be approached safely in order to send me on my way. As he edged ever closer, I decided, despite my fatigue, to put him

out of his misery, and began the walk back along the path. I
had come to the end, as far as Brancusi's sculptural ensemble
was concerned. What would I do now and where would I go?
I was still holding the sheet of paper from the Hotel
Sebastopol and looking down at it for a time, another lost
tourist studying a map – albeit one that formed an absolute
blank. For whatever reason I was reluctant to finish my
journey and I veered away from the path toward what looked
like a stone chapel. It was in fact, according to the sign over
the entrance, the Constantin Brancusi Research,
Documentation and Promotion Centre. The door was shut
fast and the entire place looked as if it had been closed for
many years. A nearby annexe, perhaps as a gesture of
goodwill, was home to a tiny bar, which consisted, as far as I
could tell of a single doorway out of which a tall bartender
would occasionally appear so as to tend a cluster of tables and
chairs neatly arranged beneath the trees. The only other
customers were a pair of teenagers who eyed me suspiciously
as I groped for a seat. I couldn't help noticing that the young
man who was no more than a boy bore an uncanny
resemblance to an image I had once seen of an adolescent
Marcel Duchamp, and it seemed suddenly strange to me that
I had never come across a picture of Brancusi as a young man.
In all of the pictures I have seen, he is always old as if he had
had no youth but, instead, woke up one morning to discover
himself older than every body around him. I dread to think of
the impression I made on the young minds of those teenagers
– I must have looked like someone they would never wish to
be. I sat slowly, facing the other way. The bartender smiled
sympathetically, took my order and returned to whatever

space there was beyond the dark opening to the bar, stooping as she stepped inside. I breathed deeply, folded my hands in my lap and gazed upwards into the branches of the yellowing beech that fanned out above my head. By its side stood another tree of the same massive proportions but it must have died because it was bearing no leaves. I scanned upwards through the inky branches to where I could see a crows nest high in the canopy. From where I was sitting the perfectly round nest looked like a bullet hole in the sky.

A drink arrived and with it my thoughts returned to earthly matters. Just as I put the glass to my lips, my eyes fell upon the shape of a yellow jacket thrown roughly over the back of a chair. I put the glass down untouched. On the table, a half-finished cigarette was smoking in an ashtray. I looked around and reached for my bag. *There you are*, I heard someone say in a local accent. I turned in my seat and found myself facing the man I had evaded three times upon my arrival in Cluj.

My god, you're white as a ghost, he said, and for a moment I thought it was true: I *had* passed away and he was, in fact, addressing a phantom or, perhaps, a photograph in a book. *Do you mind?* He said and he pulled up a metal chair, which scraped against the ground. I looked over his shoulder. The teenagers were gone and the bartender had disappeared. *You're a hard man to track down,* he said, smiling. His hair was unnaturally black, I thought, and his face was red. He wore a clean white shirt that looked as if it had just been put on and he seemed to fill the space in front of me. I had no idea what to say. He told me that his friend at the University had informed him of my visit to Romania. He wanted to ask me

227

about something I had written many years ago, some essay about a film very few people had seen. I could not remember the text he referred to but it appeared to have made a great impression on him. So much so that I couldn't tell if he was angered at my words or if they had caused him delight. For a large man, he was terribly animated. All the time he spoke his hands moved frantically as if they were connected to a separate power supply. Yet throughout our time together his face remained calm, impassive, and his voice did not crack. I had the distinct impression he was attempting to tell me something other than what he was saying. He jumped from one subject to the next so that his story was often hard to follow. He told me he preferred Giacometti's version of the Infinite Column. *It is a table leg*, he said. *Instead of holding up the unending abyss above our heads it supports a severed hand and other remnants of a dream. They have it in Paris,* he said. *In the Museum of Modern Art. It is made from plaster – not metal or stone. By now it has probably turned to dust. Still, I have a picture. You can keep it if you like.*

At one point he described in some detail the books he had written on Romanian dialects. *About this place*, he said, waving his hands about. Then he told me he had been helping an artist in Bucharest whose work consisted of smashing brightly colour china pots and reassembling them piece-by-piece. This would often take a great deal of time and, when it came to examining many of the restored artefacts, it was impossible to detect any trace of what had happened, while in others, no matter how painstaking her attempts at reassembly, there was no trace of what they had once been. Rather than the restoration of what was gone she had created something completely new. He told me he had been to England, where he hoped one day to buy a house. *A cottage*, he said. Close to the sea because he had a fondness for the sound of seagulls. He had never married and had many lovers, a fact he seemed to think would impress me in some way. After a time, I lost track of what he was saying and watched a pale butterfly move between us, its wings so white, it almost vanished as it turned in the light. *They're worried about you, back at home*, I heard him say. *Anne says that you are not sleeping. That you walk around at night. She wants you to come back.*

I looked at him and wondered how he could know such things. *What did you say?* I asked. But he smiled, then he said, *It's funny. They told me you would act this way. Who did?* I asked, my anxiety growing. *Why, the University of course.* The bartender arrived with fresh drinks and I was glad of the break in his train of thought. I wondered if now he would get to the point. He looked at me. Then he said he wanted to tell me about a dream he had when he was a child in which he saw his own death. *It was not dramatic or exciting*, he said. *I did not fall from a window or drive my car into a ravine. I did not burn in an inferno or drown at sea. In fact it was nothing like the deaths little boys imagine for themselves. In the dream I was an old man. I heard people whisper that I was very ill, but I felt no different to the way I might have done in waking life. I lay in a giant bed and gazed about me. The people at my bedside looked a long way away. One by one they began to fade into the distance until I was alone, he said. Completely alone.*

At last the hands of my companion were still. He rested

them on the table as if they were finally too heavy to hold. *Ever since that night, I have known one thing to be true,* he went on. *This was something that should never happen to a child.*

I looked at him. He stood up and put on his yellow coat. For a moment he stood beside the table and I wondered if he was going to shake my hand. Instead, he reached inside his jacket looking, for all the world, like a man reaching for a pistol. I froze and closed my eyes. When I opened them again, he was holding out a pen. *I want you to write something for me,* he said. *Please, your address.* When I get back to Bucharest I will send you a gift, and he winked. I took the pen, and tearing a page from my notebook, my hand hovered over the table. I looked up at him. *Don't tell me you have forgotten where you live? Of course not,* I said. And, closing my eyes again, I wrote without thinking, conscious only of the heavy pen scratching on the page. When I gave it to him he appeared deeply satisfied. He folded the paper away without looking at it and tucked it, along with the pen, somewhere deep inside his coat.

When I was sure he was gone, I paid the bartender, checking there were two glasses on her tray, and walked back through the gardens to where my driver was waiting in a side street not far from the Gate of the Kiss. I found him with his knees up on the dashboard, writing something in a book. He looked like Nabokov writing a novel in his American car and I wondered what part I played in the plot he was constructing. I took one last look at the arch. I realised I had no choice but to leave remainders of myself in places to which I doubted I would ever return. But if I did, I had the impression I would be restored somehow by the sheer indifference of time and space. Perhaps that is what my journey had been: a putting back together of what would never be the same. When my driver saw me he sat up and put away his book. *Cluj?* He said and I nodded. He closed the doors and drove us back toward the hills.

By the time we crossed the mountains into the countryside south of the city, it was dark. For some time I stared out at the night. It felt good to look at nothing and I thought of all the things I couldn't see. I closed my eyes and saw once more the sunlit afternoon in Târgu Jiu, my notes spread across the metal table under the trees. Looking up, I saw myself walk across the gardens. A small child ran up to me and took my hand, the sun catching her hair. The pair moved away into the light. Whoever they were they would walk through life untroubled because they would remain unknown. I watched them for a while. Then they were gone.

Photographic credits

John Latham Exhibition Image Wreckage of LTB 811F car © John Latham (Courtesy of Tate Archive)

John Latham Metropolitan Seminars in Art © Flat Time House Archive (Courtesy of Flat Time House Archive)

John Latham, Tall man wearing sunglasses: © Flat Time House Archive (Courtesy of Flat Time House Archive)

John Latham, 'Hospital' © John Latham (Courtesy of Tate Archive)

Andre Breton © Association Atelier Andre Breton (Courtesy of Association Atelier Andre Breton)

Andre Breton © Association Atelier Andre Breton (Courtesy of Association Atelier Andre Breton)

Ed Ruscha, *Royal Road Test* (book) 1967 © Ed Ruscha (Courtesy Ruscha studio.)

Ed Ruscha studio in *Leave any Information at the Signal* © Ed Ruscha (Courtesy Ruscha studio.)

Reisner/Namuth Spain c.1936 © Hans Namuth Estate, courtesy Center for Creative Photography, The University of Arizona

John Heartfield Liberty Leading the People 1936 © John J Heartfield

Joseph Cornell, Hans Namuth © Hans Namuth Estate, courtesy Center for Creative Photography, The University of Arizona

Tony Smith house models Sam Wagstaff, Talking with Tony Smith, *Artforum* Dec. 1966 © Tony Smith Estate (Courtesy of Tony Smith Estate)

Sam Wagstaff, Talking with Tony Smith, *Artforum* Dec. 1966 © Tony Smith Estate (Courtesy of Tony Smith Estate)

Sam Wagstaff, Talking with Tony Smith, *Artforum* Dec. 1966 © Tony Smith Estate (Courtesy of Tony Smith Estate)

Photocopy from 1970 Robert Morris Tate Gallery Exhibition 1971 © Tate Gallery (Courtesy of Tate Archive)

Photocopy from 1970 Robert Morris Tate Gallery Exhibition 1971 © Tate Gallery (Courtesy of Tate Archive)

Humphrey Jennings Portrait © Lee Miller Archives (Courtesy Lee Miller Archives)

Untitled (Portrait of Frank Stella), © Hollis Frampton 1963 (Courtesy Anthology Archives New York)

Michael Snow making Region Centrale 1970 © Joyce Wieland (Courtesy of the British Artists Film and video Study Collection, Central Saint Martins)

Chris Burden *Shoot* 1971 © Chris Burden (licensed by the Chris Burden Estate and DACS)

Chris Burden Shoot 1971 © Chris Burden (licensed by the Chris Burden Estate and DACS)

Constantin Brancusi *Bird in Space* c. 1930 © Succession Brancusi – All Rights Reserved. ADAGP Paris and DACS London

David Dye, Stairwell Mirror St Martins, c.1970 © David Dye (courtesy of the artist)

David Dye, *Western Reversal*, from *Studio International* 1975 © David Dye

Constantine Brancusi, *Princess X 1916* © Succession Brancusi – All Rights Reserved. ADAGP Paris and DACS London